Transformed in *Love*

Transformed

in Love

Building Your Catholic Marriage

Engaged Couple Workbook

Catholic Archdiocese of Boston

Pauline
BOOKS & MEDIA

Boston

Nihil Obstat: J. David Franks, Ph.D.
Imprimatur: ✠ Seán Cardinal O'Malley, O.F.M. Cap.
Archbishop of Boston
March 4, 2013

Natural Family Planning statistics for slide no. 25 of Topic 11 have been compiled from the following method-specific efficacy studies:

Arevalo, M., Jennings, et al., "Efficacy of a New Method of Family Planning: the Standard Day Method," *Contraception,* 65 (2002): 333–338.

Arevalo M. Jennings, et al., "Efficacy of the New TwoDay Method of Family Planning," *Fertility and Sterility,* 2004; 82:885–892.

Fehring, R. J., et al., "Efficacy of Cervical Mucus Observations Plus Electronic Hormonal Fertility Monitoring as a Method of Natural Family Planning," *Journal of Obstetric, Gynecological, and Neonatal Nursing,* 2007; 36:152–160.

Frank-Hermann, P., et al., "The Effectiveness of a Fertility Awareness Based Method to Avoid Pregnancy in Relation to a Couple's Sexual Behavior During the Fertile Time: A Prospective Longitudinal Study." *Human Reproduction,* 2007; 22:1310–1319.

J. Trussell and L. Grummer-Strawn, "Contraceptive Failure of the Ovulation Method of Periodic Abstinence," *Family Planning Perspectives,* 22 (1990): 65–75.

Cover design by Rosana Usselmann

Cover photos: istockphoto.com

Interior and slide photos: istockphoto.com; Mary Emmanuel Alves, FSP (pp. 109, 115, 118; slide nos. 3, 4, Topic 4: portrait of FSP in prayer)

ISBN-10: 0-8198-7490-6

ISBN-13: 978-0-8198-7490-0

Published by Pauline Books & Media, 50 Saint Pauls Avenue, Boston, MA 02130-3491

Printed in the U.S.A.

www.pauline.org

Pauline Books & Media is the publishing house of the Daughters of St. Paul, an international congregation of women religious serving the Church with the communications media.

1 2 3 4 5 6 7 8 9   17 16 15 14 13

Name: _____

Date: _____

Prayer for Marriage

Heavenly Father,

through the intercession of the Holy Family,

help us treasure the gift of marriage that

reflects the love of Christ for the Church,

where the self-giving love

of husband and wife

unites them more perfectly and

cooperates in your plan for

new life created in your image.

Help us support men and women

in their vocation of marriage,

especially in difficult times when

they join their sufferings to the Cross.

Help us uphold the institution of marriage

in our society as the place where

love is nurtured and family life begins.

Help us acknowledge that our future

depends on this love and on your

providential care for us. Amen.

Please pray daily for the vocation of marriage.

Nihil Obstat: Reverend Mark O'Connell, J.C.D.

Imprimatur: ✠ Seán Cardinal O'Malley, OFM Cap.
Archbishop of Boston
May 15, 2007

Contents

Foreword

My dear friends in Christ,

Allow me this moment to welcome you to *Transformed in Love: Building Your Catholic Marriage.* We are very pleased that you have chosen to marry in the Church. It is my prayer that your time preparing for marriage will be a great help to your establishing a strong foundation for your lives together and deep commitment to each other as husband and wife.

May this program, both the content and the witness of the team members, provide you with a greater understanding of the gift of faith and the practical assistance it affords us as we journey in life, no matter our vocation. I pray as well that the program provides you with a deeper appreciation of the important vocation you are entering, and that you gain additional skills to help you live out the vows you will make.

Be assured of my prayers and my gratitude for your witness to the presence of our Lord in your future marriage.

Asking God to bless you and all whom you hold dear with his abundant graces, I remain

Devotedly yours in Christ,

Seán Cardinal O'Malley, OFM Cap.
Archbishop of Boston

Acknowledgments

Many people are due thanks and recognition for the development and publication of *Transformed in Love: Building Your Catholic Marriage*. Having served as the main archdiocesan staff member charged with its development, I provide the following thanks and recognition in an effort to provide future users with a sense of the origin and development of this material. May it also, in some small measure, though in no way adequately, recognize those who have offered their generous time and talent in service to our Lord, the Archdiocese of Boston, and the vocation of marriage.

First and foremost, recognition and acknowledgment are due to Cardinal Seán O'Malley, OFM Cap., Archbishop of Boston, who initiated this program's development in order to strengthen the vocation of marriage in the Archdiocese of Boston. Without Cardinal Seán's faithful evangelical leadership and direction, *Transformed in Love* would not exist nor would it be what it is. His pastoral care and concern for all of God's people is obvious, particularly his interest and desire to help those called to the vocation of marriage.

Special thanks go next to the members of the steering committee who met regularly with me over a three year period to oversee *Transformed in Love's* development. This group truly guided the project and program to become what you have before you. The theological integrity, canonical precision, and pastoral tone is due to the expertise and commitment of the following people: the Most Reverend Walter J. Edyvean, S.T.D., Auxiliary Bishop of Boston and Episcopal Liaison for the project; the Very Rev. Mark O'Connell, J.C.D., Judicial Vicar, Ecclesiastical Court of the Archdiocese of Boston; Maria Galindez-Bianco, J.C.L., J.D., Court Judge, Ecclesiastical Court of the Archdiocese of Boston; Stephen Colella, M.A., Office for the New Evangelization of Youth and Young Adults; Mary Finnigan, Natural Family Planning Services; Angela Franks, Ph.D., Director of Theology Programs, St. John's Seminary Theological Institute for the New Evangelization; and J. David Franks, Ph.D., Professor of Sacred Theology, St. John's Seminary and Vice President for Mission, St. John's Seminary Theological Institute for the New Evangelization.

Thanks also go to an additional forty plus people who served either on the Committee on Marriage or the subsequent Marriage Preparation Recommendations Implementation Committee. Though too many to list, special thanks go to the following people for their consistent committee involvement: Rev. Thomas Griffith, SVD; Rev. Robert Masciocchi, CSS; David and Mary Brennan; Stefane and Mary Cahill Farella; Deacon James and Teresa Greer; Greg Kolodziejczak, Ph.D., Psy.D.; Michael and Whitney Pencina; Thomas and Mary Pat St. Jean; and Eileen and Christopher Wood.

Additionally, special thanks and acknowledgment go to those who helped pilot and field test *Transformed in Love*. First and foremost, thanks go to those who so faithfully and generously served as pilot team members for nearly all of the pilots: Stephen Colella, Dr. Greg Kolodziejczak, Mary Finnigan, and Eileen and Christopher Wood. Special appreciation and thanks are also due to Peter and Therese Braudis, Stefane and Mary Cahill Farella, Angela and David Franks, David and Suzanne Konieczkowski, Rev. Shawn P. Carey, and Rev. Matthew Williams who also served on many pilot teams. Without the involvement of these (and other) faithful pilot team members we would not have been able to test the program's effectiveness and work on revisions.

Thanks also go to the following for their unique contributions to the project: the Most Reverend Peter J. Uglietto, S.T.D., Auxiliary Bishop of Boston, for his consultation on the salvation history diagram and other components; Rev. Jeremy St. Martin for his articulation of the need to catechize regarding both natural and sacramental marriage; Rev. Paul O'Brien for his invaluable consultation early on in the project; Rev. Mark J. Coiro, Rev. Jonathan Gaspar, Rev. Brian Mahoney, and Rev. Matthew Williams for their contributions to the Teaching Mass material; Stefane and Mary Cahill Farella for their contributions to the temperaments and finances material and the overall tone of the program; Jeannie and Bruce Hannemann for their article on pornography in the engaged couple workbook; Thomas and Mary Pat St. Jean for their article on infertility in the engaged couple workbook; *The Faithful House*, Maternal Life International, for the inspiration to use a house as a metaphor for the program; Janet Benestad, Cabinet Secretary for Faith Formation and Evangelization, for her support; Karen Farrell for her willing and competent assistance; and Francis O'Connor, J.D., for his much needed and helpful legal advice.

Thanks also go to the Daughters of St. Paul as an entire congregation for their faithful and prayerful support of the project early on, and to the staff at Pauline Books & Media for their assistance with publication. Particular thanks go to Sr. Mary Mark Wickenhiser, FSP; Sr. Maria Grace Dateno, FSP; Sr. Sean Marie David Mayer, FSP; Sr. Carmen Christi Pompei, FSP; Sr. Kathryn James Hermes, FSP; Sr. Jackie Gitonga and the marketing team; Vanessa Reese, for her help and direction in securing permissions. Sr. Marianne Lorraine Trouvé, FSP, for her excellent developmental editing; Sr. Mary Domenica Vitello, FSP, for creating the electronic slide presentations; Rosana Usselmann for the cover design, and Sr. Linda Salvatore Boccia, FSP, for her prayerful and tireless work in designing the entire program. I thank God for the charism of the Daughters of St. Paul to communicate the Gospel through all means possible.

While the program reflects the influence of many people, singular recognition ought to be given to those who contributed substantially to the final material you have before you and who could easily be regarded as contributing authors.

Dr. Greg Kolodziejczak contributed significantly to the material on self-knowledge, communication, and the four loves. He also provided particularly insightful ways to articulate concepts within the salvation history diagram, and he influenced overall themes and threads. His professional expertise as a clinical therapist and his faithful approach was invaluable to both the human and spiritual formation elements in the program.

Drs. Angela and David Franks contributed significantly to nearly all of the theological and catechetical elements throughout the entire program and provided constant ongoing theological review. Their theological expertise mixed with practical application as a married couple and as parents yielded invaluable insights and contributions. In addition, they, together with Stephen Colella and myself, created the salvation history diagram in Topic Six.

Most significant individual thanks go to Mary Finnigan (Natural Family Planning Services) and Stephen Colella (Office for the New Evangelization) who labored with me on this project day in and day out, frequently on weeknights and weekends, for many years. As members of the Steering Committee, contributors to content, and consistent pilot team members, both, in unique ways, have provided consultation and direction to the entire program.

Mary Finnigan, in addition to being the primary author of the material on marital sexuality, could easily be regarded as the co-editor of the entire program, having intimately worked with me on every component from content to implementation. Mary provided consultation on nearly every matter and worked to shape and reshape all of the material numerous times in preparation for publication. Thanks are due to her for her constant involvement, work, and support without which the program would not be what it is.

Stephen Colella, my husband and colleague, is due thanks for his contributions on and off the clock. His professional background in theology, ministry, and training considerably influenced (in ways too numerous to list here) the content, tone, threads, and themes throughout the entire program. Personally, as my husband, I thank him for his unwavering support (both at work and at home) and for believing in the project and program. It has been a gift to me that we were able to work together on this labor of love.

Personally, I would also like to thank and acknowledge those who indirectly contributed to the project through their personal support. First and foremost, with great love and gratitude I thank my parents, Charles and Sindy Schwab, and Stephen's parents, Stephen and Cynthia Colella, for their witness of marital love and the gift of family life; our immediate and extended families and our good friends for the things they have taught us about marriage and family life; and Rev. Timothy M. Gallagher, OMV, for the ways he, and his seminars and books, have helped me to better discern God's will—particularly throughout the work on this project.

Lastly, I would be remiss not to thank Mary, our Mother, St. Joseph, St. Anthony, and all (here and in heaven) who prayed for the project. Most importantly, I thank God the Father, Son, and Holy Spirit, from whom many inspirations and consolations came and for whose glory the program exists. *Ad maiorem Dei gloriam.*

KARI J. COLELLA, MTS

Coordinator of Marriage Ministries,
Archdiocese of Boston

Introduction

Transformed in Love:
Building Your Catholic Marriage

Names of team members/people you met at the introduction:

_____   _____

_____

_____

Why are you here?

_____

_____

_____

What does it take to have a good marriage today?

_____

_____

_____

The title: *Transformed in Love*

- ❖ Marriage is a vocation through which we come to know, love, and serve God and become holy.
- ❖ God helps us through marriage and the other sacraments to become more and more transformed in love.

The subtitle: *Building Your Catholic Marriage*

- ❖ *Transformed in Love* uses a house metaphor to illustrate the concepts of establishing, building, and nurturing marriage and family life, hence its subtitle: *Building Your Catholic Marriage.*
- ❖ For each topic, we will be proposing a blueprint item, something you can do to establish, build, or nurture your marriage and family.
- ❖ You will also create your own personal blueprint and action plan of concrete things you want to do, based on each topic, to establish, build, and nurture your future together.

Throughout the program, we will be covering different topics to help you:

1. *Be wise:* Acquire knowledge about marriage and related matters.

2. *Be true:* Further discern your readiness to marry and once married, to stay committed to your vows.

3. *Be skilled:* Develop skills and gain practical tools so you can live out the promises you make on your wedding day.

4. *Be faithful:* Grow in appreciation of the role that Christian faith plays in transforming marriage into a sacrament.

We hope this program will provide you with:

1. Additional knowledge about:
   - Self
   - Fiancé/e
   - God
   - Marriage

2. An opportunity to reflect on the promises you are about to make.

3. New skills to help you do what you know you want to do and will consent to do.

4. A sense of God's presence and assistance in your relationship.

5. Some couple time.
   - This is not a retreat or a program in which your time is spent solely discussing topics with your fiancé/e.
   - We hope you will spend additional couple time before and after your wedding discussing and working with each topic.

6. An action plan/strategy.

Self-Knowledge

Who Am I? Who Are You?
We Are the Builders

"You formed my inmost being;
You knit me in my mother's womb.
I praise You, so wonderfully You made me;
Wonderful are Your works!"

PSALM 139:13–14

HOUSE METAPHOR

- Just as constructing a house requires builders, so too marriage requires builders.
- You are the builders of your marriage and family, the ones who together, with God, will establish and build your new life.

GOALS OF THIS TOPIC

- *Be wise* and *be true*: To help you deepen your knowledge of self and of your future spouse as you prepare to give yourselves to one another in marriage.
- *Be wise* and *be skilled*: To encourage:

    a. on-going self-discovery,

    b. acceptance of differences, and

    c. growth in virtue in order to improve self and love one another throughout your marriage.

What makes up who I am?

Each of us is a combination of *nature*, *nurture*, and something known as *true self*.

1. **Nature:** Our nature is our gender, disposition, and personality traits.

2. **Nurture:** Nurture is the influence environment has had on nature, how it has formed and shaped it. Our environment is made of: family of origin (our foundational experiences of love and relationships), education, culture, faith, media, habits (character, discipline, etc.).

3. **True Self:** Deeper than our nature or nurture is our *true self*, the saint God has planned us to be.

Exploring nature through temperament theory

- ❖ Temperaments are our natural dispositions and traits, hard-wired in us.
- ❖ There are four basic temperaments.
- ❖ Temperament theory has a long tradition within the Catholic Church.

Temperament theory key points

❖ All temperaments have strengths and, without moderation, can become susceptible to extremes.

❖ We cannot expect each other to react to things the same way or relate to others in an identical manner.

❖ Understanding and appreciating differences can help improve intimacy with your spouse.

❖ Marriage is not about making your spouse become like you, but helping each other to become whom God created each of you to be, with all your uniqueness and individuality.

Turn to page 10 for the Temperaments Inventory.

The Four Temperaments

Choleric	
Stereotype: The Worker	
By nature	**Susceptibilities**
Assertive	Arrogant
Born Leader	Inconsiderate
Decisive	Proud
Confident	Stubborn
Quick to react	Rigid/Inflexible
Goal oriented	Unsympathetic

Sanguine	
Stereotype: The Talker	
By nature	**Susceptibilities**
Extroverted	Impulsive
Optimistic	Overcommitted
Spontaneous	Unrealistic
Fun-loving	Indiscriminate
Enthusiastic	Unreliable
Generous	Irresponsible

Melancholic	
Stereotype: The Thinker	
By nature	**Susceptibilities**
Reflective	Pessimistic
Organized	Moody
Industrious	Indecisive
Conscientious	Demanding
Idealistic	Compulsive
Sensitive	Anxious

Phlegmatic	
Stereotype: The Watcher	
By nature	**Susceptibilities**
Calm	Unmotived
Cooperative	Complacent
Logical	Lazy
Patient	Unassertive
Flexible	Unengaged
Analytical	Apathetic

Nurture

❖ Many things form and "nurture" our nature.

❖ Nurture is the influence that *environment* has had on my nature, forming and shaping it.

❖ It is important to be aware of these influences in our own lives and in the life of our spouse.

Exploring nurture through family of origin

Our family of origin influences our:

— Attachment style

— Sense of self-worth

— Sense of roles and expectations

— Character formation

— Image of God

Our family of origin influences how we:

— Experience and express emotions

— Relate to others

— Interpret things

— Defend ourselves

— Understand the meaning of love

— Find meaning

Virtues

❖ A virtue is a habitual and firm disposition to do the good.

❖ In the Catholic tradition we highlight the following seven virtues:

1. *Prudence:* Wisdom and good judgment applied to action.

2. *Justice:* Fair treatment, that is, to give others their due, both God and neighbor.

3. *Fortitude:* Courage and perseverance.

4. *Temperance:* Moderation and self-restraint.

❖ The three most important virtues are given by God in Baptism. These are called the theological virtues.

5. *Faith:* Belief in God by the power of God.

6. *Hope:* Trusting in God that he will give us all that is for our good.

7. *Love or charity:* Loving by the power of divine love infused in our hearts.

❖ Given our temperament, we may need to develop a particular virtue, but we should strive to grow in all of them.

❖ Virtues are acquired by practice and with help from God.

❖ We need to grow in virtue to become fully who we are meant to be and to love one another well.

Vices

❖ A vice is a pattern of seeking what is not good in a particular area of life.

❖ In Christian tradition we identify the following seven vices: pride, greed, envy, anger, lust, gluttony, and sloth (or laziness).

❖ By nature, we may be inclined to one predominant vice.

❖ Vices are very destructive in marriage and family life.

True self

❖ Our true self is the truth of my personality as dreamed up by God the Father before the foundation of the world.

❖ Because of the presence of God within us through Baptism, we partake in his nature and are able to give ourselves in love to others.

Conclusion

❖ Knowing oneself is critical to being able to fully give oneself in marriage.

❖ Individual differences need to be appreciated as sources of strength in your relationship.

❖ Through practicing virtue and avoiding vice, we mature and are better able to love more fully.

❖ By virtue of the presence of God within us through Baptism, we partake in his nature and are able to give ourselves in love to others.

> "Though made of body and soul, man is one.... For by his interior qualities he outstrips the whole sum of mere things. He plunges into the depths of reality whenever he enters into his own heart; God, who probes the heart, awaits him there; there he discerns his proper destiny beneath the eyes of God."
>
> *Gaudium et Spes,* no. 14

Temperaments Inventory *

Please indicate whether any of the following words and phrases might be used to accurately summarize you or your behavior. If your response is "yes," then place a checkmark in the highlighted box. If your response is "no," do not check any box. Remember to answer how you *really are* most of the time, not how you might *want to be*.

		C	S	M	P
Example 1: Cheerful (Yes mostly, so check box.)			✓		
Example 2: Active (Not really, so leave box blank.)					
1.	Cheerful				
2.	Active				
3.	Sensitive				
4.	Calm				
5.	Talkative				
6.	Dependable				
7.	Undependable				
8.	Aggressive				
9.	Stubborn				
10.	Perfectionist				
11.	Inconsiderate				
12.	Lively				
13.	Confident				
14.	Moody				
15.	Lazy				
16.	Unsociable				
17.	Quick to react with your emotions				
18.	Process your thoughts rapidly				
19.	Take time to discern your opinion				
20.	Requires much to upset you				
21.	Fun-loving and spontaneous				
22.	Humble and hard-working				
23.	Assertive leader				
24.	Systematic and relaxed				
25.	Energized by being kind to others				
26.	Energized by fulfilling responsibilities				
27.	Energized by knowledge and sharing it				
28.	Energized by success and recognition				
TOTALS (Do not include the example) =					
Circle letter in column with the highest total =		C	S	M	P

* This inventory is merely an introduction and not tested for accuracy in determining temperament. For more in-depth inventories see Rev. Conrad Hock, *The Four Temperaments* (Milwaukee: The Bruce Publishing Co., 1958), or Art and Laraine Bennett, *The Temperament God Gave You: The Classic Key to Knowing Yourself, Getting Along with Others, and Growing Closer to the Lord* (Manchester, NH: Sophia Institute Press, 2005).

ACTIVITY

Looking at My Family of Origin

Directions: Please answer the following questions about the family environment in which you grew up. Try to circle the best answer, though in some cases you might select two answers. Try to choose an option given, but if none fit, you can add your own.

1. Affection was:

   ☐ shown generously but not in public.

   ☐ shown with the kids but not between mom and dad.

   ☐ shown between mom and dad but not with the kids.

   ☐ shown warmly and openly.

   ☐ felt but not generally expressed.

   ☐ not generally felt.

   ☐ other: _____

2. Decisions were:

   ☐ made by dad.

   ☐ made by mom.

   ☐ made by mom and dad together.

   ☐ made separately by mom and dad.

   ☐ made by the consensus of the whole family.

   ☐ not made. Indecision was the key to flexibility.

   ☐ other: _____

3. Anger was:

   ☐ expressed strongly yet productively.

   ☐ expressed gently and directly.

   ☐ expressed loudly and aggressively.

   ☐ expressed indirectly (such as by getting even in indirect ways or giving the cold shoulder).

   ☐ not expressed.

   ☐ other: _____

4. The general atmosphere in the home was:

☐ tense.

☐ serious but relaxed.

☐ hostile.

☐ somewhat raucous and fun.

☐ warm and loving.

☐ other: _____

5. My parents tried to resolve their disagreements:

☐ by one caving in to the other.

☐ through lively arguing and debate.

☐ through thoughtful discussion and compromise.

☐ through hostile confrontation.

☐ by avoiding the issue or "sweeping it under the rug."

☐ they seldom if ever disagreed.

☐ other: _____

6. I would describe the overall home environment as:

☐ quite messy.

☐ neat and clean.

☐ somewhat messy but comfortable.

☐ impeccable.

☐ squalor.

☐ other: _____

7. House rules were:

☐ made to be broken.

☐ sensible and flexible.

☐ strict and strictly enforced.

☐ nonexistent.

☐ other: _____

8. Family togetherness was:

   ☐ a source of joy.

   ☐ suffocating. It made it hard for people to be themselves.

   ☐ artificial. We were going through the motions.

   ☐ insufficient. I wanted more togetherness.

   ☐ other: _____

9. Uncomfortable issues were:

   ☐ kept strictly secret.

   ☐ discussed thoughtfully and respectfully.

   ☐ awkwardly avoided.

   ☐ sources of ongoing conflict.

   ☐ None of these. We had no uncomfortable issues.

   ☐ other: _____

10. The best way to feel emotionally safe and secure, especially during times of conflict, was to:

    ☐ keep others happy.

    ☐ make sure I was almost perfect.

    ☐ make sure I was strong.

    ☐ get away from the family.

    ☐ None of these. We felt emotionally secure without much effort.

    ☐ other: _____

PERSONAL NOTES

TOPIC 2

Communication

Our Relationship Needs Some TLC:
Skills for Building

"Whoever answers
before listening,
theirs is folly and
shame."

PROVERBS 18:13

HOUSE METAPHOR

- ✌ Just as builders of a house need the right skills and tools, you need skills and tools to build a marriage and family.

- ✌ Good communication is an essential skill and tool for building a great marriage and family.

GOAL OF THIS TOPIC

- ✌ *Be skilled*: To provide you with concrete communication skills and principles to help you grow in intimacy now and throughout your marriage.

Effective Communication

1. Effective communication is a learned skill.

2. Effective communication requires:

  ❖ Intention

  ❖ Effort

  ❖ Practice

3. Effective communication has three steps: **TLC**

  Step 1 = Effective **T**alking

  Step 2 = Effective **L**istening

  Step 3 = Effective **C**hecking

TLC Skills

Step 1 = Effective **T**alking

  ❖ Make a complaint, not a criticism.

  ❖ Begin with an underlying positive.

  ❖ Avoid generalizations.

  ❖ Communicate in bite size chunks.

  ❖ Use "I" statements.

Step 2 = Effective **L**istening

❖ Listen to understand, rather than merely listening to respond.

❖ Be empathic and try to see things from the other person's perspective, what it's like *for the other*.

❖ Understanding is not agreement.

Step 3 = Effective **C**hecking

❖ Articulate understanding.

❖ The listener asks the talker if he or she understood correctly.

❖ Be open to correction.

❖ The talker should clarify to help the listener "get it."

❖ Switch roles!

Seven Principles of Effective Communication

1. Listen and express yourself effectively.

2. Be curious rather than judgmental.

3. Be thoughtfully responsive rather than emotionally reactive.

4. Be aware that your interpretation does not necessarily reflect your spouse's intent.

5. Be aware of interactive patterns in your relationship.

6. Be aware of timing.

7. Persevere.

Closing Thoughts

❖ Use these communication skills to expand your general communication toolbox: at work, with extended family, with children, etc.

❖ Start small, build skills.

❖ Separate problem discussion from problem solution.

❖ Use TLC to talk about both positive and negative things to build intimacy.

RESOURCE: DECISION-MAKING

How Do We Make Decisions?

The process proposed below is a common decision making process that incorporates some of St. Ignatius of Loyola's writings on decision-making. Making a decision can include two phases: 1) problem discussion and 2) problem solution.

1. Problem Discussion:

  ❖ Make sure you have used TLC to discuss the problem or issue first.

  ❖ Effective communication skills form the foundation for effective decision-making.

  ❖ Often solutions present themselves simply by listening to understand—thereby overcoming misinterpretations and misconceptions. In these cases the decision becomes obvious through discussion.

2. Problem Solution:

Couples should move into the problem solution phase only after the decision to be made is thoroughly understood, taking into account each person's perspective, experience, and feelings. Each person needs to have the opportunity to fully express his or her perspective, and to feel fully understood.[1]

Process for Problem Solution [2]

(See Problem Solution Worksheet, p. 22.)

1. Frame the decision as a question.

  ❖ Agree together that this one question needs to be decided.

  ❖ Make sure to keep to the question posed.

  Example 1: Where do we spend Christmas?

  Example 2: Do we send the kids to Catholic school?

  Example 3: Should we try to have another child?

---

1. These two phases are frequently proposed in communications skills techniques. See also *Relationship Enhancement Program, Mastering the Mysteries of Love,* and *PREP.*

2. For more on this topic, a good resource is Timothy Gallagher, OMV, *Discerning the Will of God: An Ignatian Guide to Christian Decision Making* (New York: Crossroad Publishing Co., 2009).

2. Approach the decision in prayer, seeking to do God's will.

❖ Pray that God will direct you and reveal his will. (Prayer is the context and a part of each following step. See Topic 9 (p. 89), for additional practical ways to pray and discern God's will.)

❖ Some matters of decision-making are weightier and more significant. Moral decisions fall into this category.

❖ It is most important that we are discerning between two or more good options, not between moral and immoral options.

❖ When seeking God's will for a specific decision, there are three ways we can know God's will:

1. Church teaching: Does Church teaching provide an answer to the decision you need to make? You can be sure you are doing God's will by following Church teaching.

2. Clarity without doubt: There are some things that God clearly reveals to us so that we do not doubt and we know a specific course of action we are to follow. We have an internal sense; "we just know" we are to proceed in a certain manner.

3. Clarity over time: God may reveal his will through many different experiences over time. We may not have a single experience of absolute clarity, but a pattern of experiences that consistently draw us to one option. This pattern brings peace and confirmation over time.

❖ If the matter at hand is not clearly answered in these three ways, then continue with the following steps.

3. Brainstorm all possible solutions.

❖ Write down all possible solutions, no matter how logical, possible, or reasonable they are.

❖ Do not criticize or comment on your spouse's suggestions.

❖ Brainstorming options is a proven method to help people find solutions that were not obvious in the beginning.

4. Use TLC to discuss the possible solutions that were brainstormed.

❖ Go back over the list you brainstormed and discuss it using TLC.

❖ Remove options that now appear unrealistic or not possible.

❖ Choose the best options and then move to the next step.

5. Write down the "pros" and "cons" of each option.

❖ Write down the advantages and disadvantages of answering "yes" or "no."

❖ You will have four columns: pros and cons of answering "yes" and pros and cons of answering "no."

Ex. 1: Should we try to have another child?

Column 1 = Pros of having another child.

Column 2 = Cons of having another child.

Column 3 = Pros of not having another child.

Column 4 = Cons of not having another child.

6. Discuss the columns.

❖ Once all the pros and cons have been written down, go back to the TLC skills to discuss the pros and cons.

❖ Evaluate if one option seems to be better than another, and if the process has brought to light which option seems right.

❖ Remember it is not the number of answers in a given column that is of ultimate importance, but the weight of the answers.

7. Choose your decision and write it down.

❖ Together, decide which option you both choose.

❖ Write the decision down.

8. Make a plan for implementing the decision.

❖ Write down the details of how the decision will get implemented:

— Who

— Does what

— When

9. Seek confirmation and agree to follow-up.

❖ Ask God to confirm your decision with peace and freedom.

❖ Set a date for following-up on the choice and the decision to make sure it is the right one.

If Steps 1–9 are not enough, here are some additional suggestions to help you decide what to do:

✓ Consider how you would advise someone else.

❖ If someone you know had to make the same decision, and they told you all that you now know from doing the previous steps, consider how you would advise them to proceed and choose that option yourself.

✓ Mentally, try each option on for size.

    ❖ If you are still having difficulty, try mentally choosing one option and see how it feels to you over the course of the day or over a couple of days.

    ❖ Notice how you feel about the decision: Are you at peace? Does it seem right? Do you feel confirmed in the decision? Does it not feel right? Are you uncomfortable?

✓ Imagine yourself on death's door or standing before God, and consider which option you would have liked to have chosen at that point in your life.

    ❖ Sometimes imagining ourselves at death's door or even standing before God can help us to have a good perspective on what ultimately matters. If, in imagining yourself at the end of your life, you wish you had chosen one option or another, then pick that one.

✓ Seek advice from people who can help you make a decision that brings glory to God.

    ❖ Sometimes outside advice can be very helpful.

    ❖ Seek advice from people you trust and who have similar values.

✓ Offer God each option and notice how you feel.

    ❖ Pretend you are actually presenting one option at a time to God.

    ❖ As you present each option, pay attention to how you feel and what stirs in you as you present it to God.

PROBLEM SOLUTION WORKSHEET

1. Frame the decision as a question.

   _____

2. Approach the decision in prayer, seeking to do God's will.

   ❖ Prayer is the context and a part of each following step.

3. Brainstorm all possible solutions.

   ❖ Write down all possible solutions, no matter how logical, possible, or reasonable they are.

   ❖ Do not criticize or comment on your spouse's suggestions. Brainstorming options is a proven method to help people find solutions that were not obvious in the beginning.

Possible answers: _____

_____

_____

_____

_____

4. Use TLC to discuss the possible solutions that were brainstormed.

   ❖ Go back over the list you brainstormed and discuss it using TLC.

   ❖ Remove options that now appear unrealistic or not possible.

   ❖ Choose the best options and then move to the next step.

5. Write down the pros and cons of each option.

Pros for "yes"	Cons for "yes"	Pros for "no"	Cons for "no"

6. Discuss the columns.

❖ Take time to talk about what you like and dislike about each option.

❖ Use the TLC method.

7. Choose your decision and write it down. Make sure you both agree to the solution.

❖ Our decision: _____

_____

_____

8. Make a plan for implementing the decision.

❖ Write down the details of how the solution will get implemented.

Who: _____

Does what: _____

When: _____

9. Seek confirmation and agree to follow-up.

❖ Ask God to confirm your decision with peace and freedom.

❖ Set a date for following-up on the choice and the plan to make sure it is working.

Date for follow-up: _____

ACTIVITY
COMMUNICATION SKILLS PRACTICE

Directions:

1. TALKING: One person is the talker. Choose an issue that has some emotion for you, but is not volatile. Here are some simple possibilities:

❖ What do you think about the program so far, and why?

❖ What feelings surface when you think about your wedding day, and why?

2. LISTENING: The other person is the listener and empathically responds. To get you oriented in the right direction, you may want to begin your response with:

❖ "It sounds like you feel _____

because _____."

❖ "It seems that you feel _____

because _____."

❖ "You feel _____

because _____."

❖ Or think to yourself (but preferably don't say out loud): "What I hear you saying is . . . ," and then summarize the thoughts and feelings that were expressed.

3. CHECKING: Check to see if the response was accurate. For example, "Did I get that right?" or "Did I understand you correctly?" Make adjustments to the empathic response as needed.

4. SWITCH ROLES: The talker now listens and the listener becomes the talker, again checking to see if the empathic response was accurate. You can continue going back and forth multiple times, as needed or desired.

TOPIC 3

Expectations

What Are We Expecting?
What Will Our Marriage Be Like?

"Hope deferred makes
the heart sick,
but a wish fulfilled is a
tree of life."

PROVERBS 13:12

ᔕ Just as potential homeowners need to articulate expectations regarding their desires, so too you have to discover and share your expectations with one another regarding your future marriage and family.

GOALS OF THIS TOPIC

ᔕ *Be wise*: To understand the role expectations play in marriage.

ᔕ *Be skilled*: To provide practical suggestions for managing expectations well.

Definitions of an expectation

❖ Outlook, prospect, a belief about or a mental picture of the future.

❖ Anticipation: looking forward to something with the confidence of fulfillment.

❖ The feeling that something is about to happen.

Expectations can come from

❖ Self

❖ Family

❖ Culture

❖ Faith/religious tradition

❖ Other relationships

The importance of expectations in marriage

❖ Our happiness in marriage is often tied to how well our expectations are met.

❖ How we manage expectations is very important!

Five steps to managing expectations

1. Be aware of what you expect.
2. Be clear about what you expect.
3. Listen to your spouse.
4. Listen to the Lord.
5. If needed, make modifications.

ACTIVITY
EXPLORING OUR EXPECTATIONS

Directions: Work in separate rooms or spaces. Please answer the first two questions of each section (those in italics). This will allow you time to cover every section. After completing the questions in italics go back over the list and indicate the top three items you think are the most important to discuss with your fiancé/e. If you have more time, answer the rest of the questions. In a few minutes we will invite you to reconnect and share your answers. Complete the unfinished sections at home and commit to sharing your answers with one another.

1. How do you expect to celebrate special occasions . . .

Birthdays? _____

_____

Anniversaries? _____

_____

Christmas Eve? Day? _____

_____

Thanksgiving? _____

_____

Triduum/Easter? _____

_____

Valentine's Day? _____

_____

Vacations? _____

_____

Holy days of obligation? _____

_____

Other events or occasions? _____

_____

_____

_____

_____

2. Who will do the . . .

Bills? _____

_____

Laundry? _____

_____

Cleaning? _____

_____

House maintenance? _____

_____

Car maintenance? _____

_____

Grocery shopping? _____

_____

Cooking? _____

_____

Driving? _____

_____

3. What about children . . .

How soon will we have children? _____

_____

How many? _____

_____

Names? _____

_____

Public/Private/Catholic/Home School? _____

_____

Other expectations regarding children? _____

_____

_____

4. What about work . . .

What type of work would be best suited to your family life? _____

_____

Do you want one parent to stay home when you have young children? Who?

_____

Do you want one parent to stay home when older children are home (i.e. after school)? _____

_____

Will careers/priorities change depending on family needs? _____

_____

5. What about in-laws and extended family . . .

How often do you expect to see your family? _____

_____

How often do you expect to see your fiancé/e's family? _____

_____

How involved would you like them to be as grandparents, aunts, uncles, etc.?

_____

How involved do you think they would like to be as grandparents, aunts, uncles, etc.? _ _____

_____

Who keeps in touch with each set of in-laws? How? _____

_____

What about care for elderly/infirm parents and family members? _____

_____

6. Other expectations you have . . . _____

_____

_____

_____

_____

7. The program has already introduced self-knowledge and communication as topics that are important as you prepare for marriage. Upcoming topics cover: what love is, what marriage is, what sacramental marriage is, the vows you will make, marital sexuality, finances, important spiritual practices for marriage and family life, and how to keep love alive. These are good areas to discuss in terms of expectations. Please list any other expectations you would like to discuss in any of these areas.

_____

_____

_____

_____

_____

_____

What Is Love?

Seeking the Good of the Other: Making Our House a Home

"God is love,
and whoever remains
in love
remains in God
and God in him."

1 JOHN 4:16

HOUSE METAPHOR

- A house is typically understood to be a structure or building where people reside.
- A home connotes something more personal: a sense of belonging, an emotional connection, a place we feel comfortable.
- Love makes a house feel like a home.

GOALS OF THIS TOPIC

- *Be wise*: To provide you with an understanding of the different types of love.
- *Be true*: To provide you with an understanding of the need for mature, self-giving love in marriage in order to maintain true love throughout your marriage.

ACTIVITY

Directions: Answer the two questions below by completing as many statements as you like. We will ask volunteers to share answers.

1. What is *love*?

Love is: _____

_____

_____

_____

_____

_____

_____

_____

_____

_____

_____

2. Why do you love your fiancé/e?

I love my fiancé/e because: _____

_____

_____

_____

_____

_____

_____

_____

_____

_____

_____

_____

Four different types of love

1. *Storge:* Affection/based on familiarity.

2. *Philia:* Friendship/based on shared interests.

3. *Eros:* Includes romantic love/based on desire.

   ❖ *Eros* seeks union with whatever it desires.

   ❖ *Eros* is often what draws a couple toward marriage.

   ❖ *Eros* is good and natural, "rooted in man's very nature," and is part of God's design for man and woman.[1]

4. *Agape:* Sacrificial/unconditional love is *not based on self* but on the *other*.

   ❖ *Agape* is sacrificial and unconditional love.

   ❖ *Agape* is not based on feeling; it is based on a choice/decision.

   ❖ *Agape* is the highest form of love, consummating all other forms.

"To love is to will the good of another."

— St. Thomas Aquinas [2]

---

1. Pope Benedict XVI, *Deus Caritas Est* (Boston: Pauline Books & Media, 2006), 11.

2. CCC no. 1766, which references St. Thomas Aquinas, STh I-II, 26, 4.

❖ A "progression of love" occurs in a relationship that is oriented toward marriage.

❖ *Agape* does not come easily to us. We need God's help to love like this.

A healthy marriage encompasses all four types of love

❖ Marital love is rooted in *agape* love, love that seeks the good of the other.

❖ To choose the good of the other, to love selflessly and with true concern for the well-being of another, will keep love alive throughout the marriage.

What Is Marriage?

*God's Plan for Love and Life:
The Architect's Design*

"That is why a man leaves
his father and mother
and clings to his wife,
and the two of them
become one body."

GENESIS 2:24

HOUSE METAPHOR

◦ Just as builders need to understand the architect's plans, so too we need to understand how God, the architect of marriage, designed it so we can build and maintain a successful marriage.

GOAL OF THIS TOPIC

◦ *Be wise* and *be true*: To help you gain a more complete understanding of marriage as a natural institution, in order to better understand the vows you will make and the way of life you are choosing.

"The matrimonial covenant, by which a man and a woman establish between themselves a partnership of the whole of life and which is ordered by its nature to the good of the spouses and the procreation and education of offspring, has been raised by Christ the Lord to the dignity of a sacrament between the baptized."

Code of Canon Law, canon 1055

GROUP ACTIVITY

Directions: Working together with those nearby, answer these four questions and write your answers in the space provided. We will ask the small groups to share their answers with the larger group.

Aristotle said one should ask four fundamental questions to gain a precise understanding of anything.

They are:	For example, consider a table.
1. What *is* it?	1. A table *is* a flat surface raised by four legs.
2. What is it *made of*?	2. A table is *made of* wood, plastic, etc.
3. What is it *for*?	3. A table is *for* various tasks: to put things on, to write on, etc.
4. Where does it *come from*?	4. A table *comes from* a factory, trees, etc.

1. What *is* marriage? _____

_____

_____

2. What is marriage *made of*? _____

_____

_____

3. What is marriage *for*? _____

_____

_____

4. Where does marriage *come from*? _____

_____

_____

Marriage *is* a covenant and a partnership of the whole of life.

a. Covenant.

❖ A covenant is a solemn agreement that defines and establishes a permanent relationship between persons, or between persons and God.

❖ The Bible contains many examples of covenants, such as those between God and Abraham, and Christ and the Church.

❖ A covenant is a matter of self-gift, has unqualified obligations and responsibilities, and is for an unlimited amount of time.

b. Partnership of the whole of life.

❖ Marriage is a partnership in which the *two* become *one*, forming one heart and soul.

❖ Marriage is a partnership in which everything is shared.

❖ Marriage is permanent and indissoluble.

Marriage *is made of* one man and one woman and their mutual consent later consummated by becoming "one flesh."

a. Man and woman.

❖ Men and women are *different* but *equal* in human dignity.

❖ Men and women "complement" each other.

❖ The very bodies of males and females reveal that we are made to be in relationship.

❖ Both men and women are necessary for life to continue.

b. Mutual consent requires:

❖ *Freedom:* Both parties freely consent. They should not feel coerced or pressured by anyone. They must also be free from any previous bonds or other legal restrictions.

❖ *Ability:* Both parties have the ability both to understand and to live out the nature and purposes of marriage.

❖ *Intention:* Both parties intend to enter marriage.

❖ *Equality:* Both parties enter the marriage without an inequality in status that would compromise the freedom of consent.

c. What the couple consent to with their words in the ceremony, they consummate with their bodies by becoming one flesh.

Marriage *is for* the good of the spouses and having and raising children.

❖ Marriage has two purposes: the good of the spouses *and* having and raising children.

❖ Marriage is *for* nurturing *love* and *life*!

❖ The two purposes go hand in hand. We cannot separate them.

a. Good of the spouses.

❖ Social science studies reveal that married people are, on average, happier, healthier, and wealthier than single people.[1]

❖ Marriage helps us become better people.

b. Having and raising children.

❖ Marriage is meant to be fruitful.

❖ Marriage and marital love is not just about creating new life; it is also about nurturing and educating that new life.

❖ Infertile couples are also called to be generous with their love. Since the spirit of marital love is fruitful, all married men and women, whether or not they are able to have biological children, need to discern what being fruitful means for them.

Marriage *comes from* God and from the couple's mutual consent.

a. The institution comes from God.

❖ "God himself is the author of marriage."[2]

❖ God created marriage at the beginning of time for all people.

❖ God also created our particular marriage. He brought us together. He authored our love from before the foundation of the world.

b. And a couple's mutual consent. (See the information on consent, p. 38.)

❖ If one or both parties intentionally exclude certain purposes or deny certain properties, a marriage does not take place.

❖ For example, a marriage does not take place if:

— someone does not intend a partnership for the whole of life.

— someone does not intend permanence.

— someone does not intend the good of the other.

— someone is not open to children.

We will see later how the vows relate to these properties and purposes.

---

1. See Linda Waite and Maggie Gallagher, *The Case for Marriage: Why Married People Are Happier, Healthier, and Better Off Financially* (New York: Doubleday, 2000).

2. CCC no. 1603.

What Is Sacramental Marriage?

You, Me, and Jesus:
Our Marriage Transformed By
and Radiating His Love

"I give you a new commandment:
love one another.
As I have loved you,
so you also should love one another."
JOHN 13:34

HOUSE METAPHOR

- ✄ Just as love transforms a house into a home, so too, Jesus transforms natural marriage into sacramental marriage.

GOALS OF THIS TOPIC

- ✄ *Be wise*: To help you gain a better understanding of how and why marriage between Christians is a sacrament.
- ✄ *Be faithful*: To help you grow in your appreciation of the Christian faith and the way in which sacraments can help us to become more transformed in love.

"The matrimonial covenant, by which a man and a woman establish between themselves a partnership of the whole of life and which is ordered by its nature to the good of the spouses and the procreation and education of offspring, has been raised by Christ the Lord to the dignity of a sacrament between the baptized."

Code of Canon Law, canon 1055

GOD THE FATHER'S LOVE FOR US

In order to understand how marriage is a sacrament between a baptized man and a baptized woman, we first need to understand the sacraments. The best way to understand the sacraments and the role they play in life is to review the story of God's love for us as revealed over time. Once we better understand the sacraments, we can better understand marriage as a sacrament and what that means and what difference that makes.

God the Father's love for us begins with God

❖ God himself is a relationship of love. The one God is three Persons: the Father, the Son, and the Holy Spirit.

❖ The love between the Father and the Son is the Holy Spirit.

❖ Each Person of the Trinity is distinct, and at the same time the three Persons are united.

❖ God's very nature is relational.

God created us

❖ In a plan of sheer gratuitous love, God the Father created the universe. He did so to set the stage for each one of us. He wills the eternal happiness of every single human person.

❖ God the Father created us to be in relationship, friendship with him and to share in his love.

❖ God created us to be in relationship with others.

❖ God created us with free will.

❖ We are made for love, but true love can only be freely given and received.

The Fall

❖ We turned away from God. We call this the Fall.

❖ Our human nature is wounded by the Fall, not destroyed.

❖ As a consequence of the Fall, we are conceived in a state of original sin.

God the Father remains faithful to us

❖ God the Father did not abandon us. He continued to reach out to us and love us.

❖ God chose to reveal his goodness through the people of Israel.

❖ God promised a Messiah and salvation from our sins.

❖ God promised to restore us to right relationship with him, to restore loving intimacy with him.

God the Father's love for us revealed by Jesus, his Son

❖ God became man.

❖ Jesus Christ is "God made flesh"—God the Son became a man and lived among us.

❖ Jesus shows us the Father's unconditional love for us, and shows us how to love.

❖ The predicament caused by sin is so dire only God can heal us.

❖ Jesus died on the cross to atone for the debt of our sins, and so brings about the forgiveness of our sins.

❖ Jesus rose from the dead, completing the work of our redemption, so that we might die to sin and rise to a new life with him—enacting and revealing love without limit.

❖ Jesus loved us to the end, loved us unto death.

❖ Through Jesus's life, death, and resurrection, we learn more about:

   1. what true love is;

   2. how very much God loves us; and

   3. how we are to love one another in marriage.

❖ Jesus told us to: "love one another as I have loved you" (John 13:34). This love is:

   1. *Free:* freely given, freely received, unconditional;

   2. *Total:* total self-gift, 100 percent;

   3. *Faithful:* committed until death;

   4. *Fruitful:* moves beyond self, bears fruit;

   5. *Sacrificial:* for others; dying to self.

Jesus gains eternal life for us, now and forever

❖ Eternal life is participation in God's life and love.

New life in Christ through Baptism

❖ Through Baptism we become part of God's love story, and he becomes part of ours.[1]

❖ Through Baptism, sin is forgiven.

❖ Through Baptism, we receive the Holy Spirit.[2]

❖ Through Baptism, we become part of God's family.

❖ Through Baptism, we become disciples of Jesus.

Struggle

❖ Baptism does not mean we no longer sin or experience the effects of sin.

❖ Our lives are not a straight trajectory to heaven, with no bumps along the way.

❖ The life of Christian discipleship is marked by constant effort on our part, always under the sweet impulse of grace, to overcome sin and be transformed in love.

❖ We still have hope.

❖ There is no reason to fear or become discouraged with our weaknesses, because God the Father does not leave us alone on the journey.

God helps us through grace

❖ God gives us his *grace*.

❖ Grace is God's "free and undeserved help" in our lives.[3]

❖ One way God gives us his grace is through the Holy Spirit within us.

❖ God gives us the Church, through which we receive his grace and help.

❖ The primary way the Church communicates God's grace is through the sacraments.

---

1. See CCC nos. 1213–1284, particularly nos. 1213, 1257.
2. See CCC no. 1262.
3. CCC no. 1996.

God the Father's Love for Us

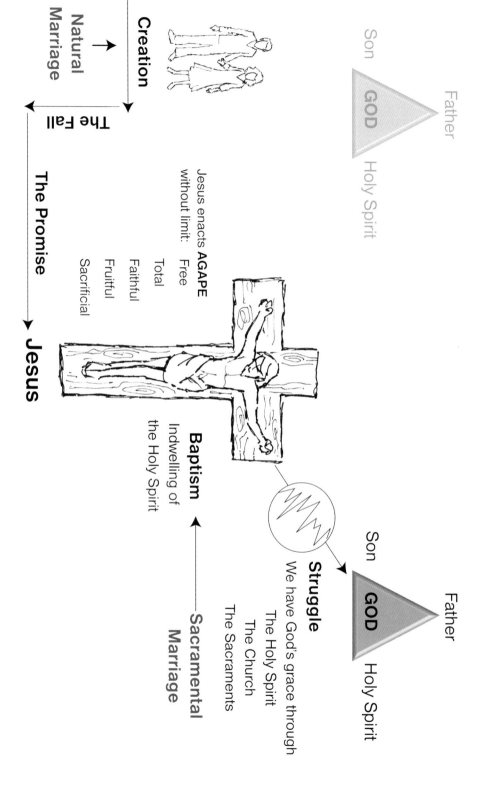

SACRAMENTS

Sacraments of Initiation	Sacraments of Healing	Sacraments at the Service of Communion
Baptism	Penance and Reconciliation	Holy Orders
Confirmation	Anointing of the Sick	Marriage
Eucharist		

A sacrament *is* a) an outward sign and b) a means of grace.[4]

a) **Outward sign**: Each sacrament is a unique sign. They are visible; we can see them.

b) **Means of grace**: Every sacrament gives grace; the sacraments establish or intensify our friendship with God and bring us God's free and undeserved help.

A sacrament *is made of* a) a certain kind of *matter* and b) is performed according to the *form* required.

a) **Matter**: Each sacrament has its own matter, its own elements and gestures.

b) **Form**: And each sacrament must be celebrated according to the way in which the Church says it needs to be done using the prescribed ritual words; this is called the "form" of the sacrament.

A sacrament *is for* a) growth in holiness, b) building up the Church, and c) the worship and glory of God.[5]

a) **Growth in holiness**: To grow in holiness is to be perfected in love. Sacraments enable us to become more Christ-like and holy, to become the saints the Father has always desired us to be.

b) **Building up the Church**: As members become more transformed in the self-giving love of Christ, they become more active in the Church and in drawing

---

4. See CCC nos. 1131, 1145–1152.
5. CCC no. 1123.

others to Christ. Fully alive in Christ, we can't help but try to share with others the joy we experience. This is called evangelization.

c) **Worship and glory of God**: Living in a Christ-like way—true love in action—gives glory to God.

A sacrament *comes from* Jesus through the Church.

Jesus instituted all of the sacraments during his earthly life.[6]

---

6. See CCC nos. 1114, 1131, 1210.

SACRAMENTAL MARRIAGE

Sacramental marriage *is* a covenant and partnership of the whole of life. It is also a) *a sign of Christ's love for the Church* **and b)** *a means of grace.*

a) **A sign of Christ's love for the Church:**

   ❖ Christian couples say: "I love you as Christ loves the Church, and I give myself to and for you as Christ gives himself to and for the Church in a way that is free, total, faithful, fruitful, and sacrificial."

b) **A means of grace:**[7]

   ❖ Christ dwells with them and is the source of grace.

   ❖ The graces proper to the sacrament help the couple to:

   — love each other with Jesus's love;

   — forgive one another;

   — bear one another's burdens;

   — pick up their crosses and follow Jesus;

   — love one another with supernatural, tender, and fruitful love;

   — attain holiness in their married life;

   — welcome and educate their children.

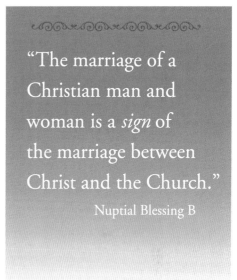

"The marriage of a Christian man and woman is a *sign* of the marriage between Christ and the Church."

Nuptial Blessing B

Sacramental marriage *is made of* a) a *baptized* **man and a** *baptized* **woman and b) their mutual consent** *exchanged in a valid way* **and consummated by becoming one flesh.**

a) **Matter:** The matter of the sacrament of marriage is the Christian man and woman and their mutual consent, which they consummate by becoming one flesh.

b) **Form:** The form of marriage is the way in which the Christian man and woman exchange their vows.

   ❖ Catholics must exchange their vows in a way recognized by the Catholic Church, for example in a Catholic ceremony in a Catholic church or, with the proper permission, in another approved way.

---

7. See CCC no. 1642.

Sacramental marriage *is for* the good of the spouses and having and raising children. It is also for a) *growth in holiness*, b) *building up the Church*, and c) *worshiping and glorifying God*.

a) **Growth in holiness:**

❖ Our responsibility in marriage is to bring not only ourselves but our spouse and children to heaven.

❖ Everything within marriage, all the trials and joys, obligations and choices have the potential to help us grow in holiness and become the saints God wants us to be.

b) **Building up the Church:**

❖ The witness of holy marriages spreads the Gospel to children and can draw others to Christ and his Church.

c) **Worshiping and glorifying God:**

❖ Christ-like marriages, in themselves, give glory to God, for the glory of God shines out above all in works of true love.

Sacramental marriage *comes from* God the Father and from *Jesus through the Church*, and from the couple's mutual consent.

❖ Jesus was at a wedding in Cana and performed his first miracle there (see John 2:1–12).

❖ When the wedding couple ran out of wine, he took a good thing, water, and turned it into something even better: wine!

❖ Water ⇨ wine; natural ⇨ supernatural!

❖ He also takes the great thing that marriage is and raises it to a sacrament.

❖ The bride and groom are the ministers of the marriage, and if their marriage is a sacrament, ministers of the sacrament as well.

❖ The priest or deacon is required as an official Church witness, but technically he does not "marry you."

Conclusion

❖ God created marriage at the beginning of human history for all people as a means of nurturing love and life.

❖ For Christians, marriage is also a sacrament.

❖ It is a sign of Jesus's love for the Church and a means of his grace.

❖ God the Father loves us so much that he gives us our spouse and allows us to share in divine love.

❖ It is beautiful that every individual love story is part of this bigger love story: God's love for us.

SUMMARY

Marriage

1. *Is* a covenant and a partnership of the whole of life.

2. *Is made of* one man and one woman and their mutual consent later consummated by becoming "one flesh."

3. *Is for* the good of the spouses and having and raising children.

4. *Comes from* God and from the couple's mutual consent.

A sacrament

1. *Is* an outward sign and a means of grace.

2. *Is made of* a certain kind of matter and is performed according to the form required.

3. *Is for* growth in holiness, building up the Church, and the worship and glory of God.

4. *Comes from* Jesus through the Church.

Sacramental marriage

1. *Is* a covenant and a partnership of the whole of life. It is also a sign of Christ's love for the Church and a means of grace.

2. *Is made of* a baptized man and a baptized woman and their mutual consent exchanged in a valid way and consummated by becoming one flesh.

3. *Is for* the good of the spouses and having and raising children. It is also for growth in holiness, building up the Church, and worshiping and glorifying God.

4. *Comes from* God the Father and from Jesus through the Church, and from the couple's mutual consent.

The *graces* proper to the sacrament help the couple to:

❖ love each other with Jesus's love;

❖ forgive one another;

❖ bear one another's burdens;

❖ pick up their crosses and follow Jesus;

❖ love one another with supernatural, tender, and fruitful love;

❖ attain holiness in their married life;

❖ welcome and educate their children.[8]

---

8. CCC nos. 1641–1642.

PERSONAL NOTES

TOPIC 7

The Rite of Marriage

I Do, Do You?
The Promises We Make and Live

"So they are no longer two, but one flesh. Therefore, what God has joined together, no human being must separate."

MATTHEW 19:6

HOUSE METAPHOR

- ∽ Buying a house usually requires a contract.

- ∽ Marriage is more than a contract; it is a covenant brought into being through the vows you will profess and consummate.

GOALS OF THIS TOPIC

- ∽ *Be wise* and *be true*: To help you understand and reflect upon the vows you will be making in the Rite of Marriage.

- ∽ *Be wise* and *be skilled*: To help you understand the elements of the marriage celebration so that you can plan a celebration that is personally expressive and reflects the Church's vision for marriage.

CEREMONY OPTIONS

Who	What	How	Why the recommendation?
Two Catholics	Sacramental Marriage	Recommended within Mass	Their first act as a married couple is to receive the Body and Blood of our Lord and allows attendees (who presumably are mostly Catholic) the opportunity to receive the Eucharist as well.
Catholic and Baptized	Sacramental Marriage	Recommended outside of Mass	Out of respect for the non-Catholic party (and presumably their family) who would not be receiving Holy Communion.
Catholic and Non-Baptized	Valid Natural Marriage	Recommended outside of Mass	Out of respect for the non-Catholic party (and presumably their family) who would not be receiving Holy Communion.

THE CELEBRATION OF MARRIAGE

ENTRANCE RITES

Gathering	
Welcome of Bride and Groom	At the door of the church or at the altar.
Procession Options	Both bride and groom accompanied by parents, preceded by ushers, bridesmaids, and presiding clergy
	Both bride and groom accompanied by parents, preceded by ushers and bridesmaids
	Bride accompanied by parents preceded by ushers and bridesmaids
	Bride accompanied by father preceded by ushers and bridesmaids
	Many choices for the entrance song
Greeting	
Penitential Act (within Mass)	
Opening Prayer (Collect)	

LITURGY OF THE WORD

Old Testament Reading	Nine options
	Choice of reader
Responsorial Psalm	Seven options
	Choice of reader/cantor
	Choice of many musical settings
New Testament Reading	Thirteen options
	Choice of reader
Gospel Acclamation	Choice of musical settings
Gospel	Ten options (proclaimed by deacon or priest)
Homily	Based on the Scriptures, Church teaching on marriage, and the couple's lives

RITE OF MARRIAGE IN DETAIL

Address to the Couple	
Questions Regarding Intentions	❧ "N. _____ and N. _____, have you come here freely and without reservation to give yourselves to each other in marriage?" ❧ "Will you love and honor each other as man and wife for the rest of your lives?" ❧ "Will you accept children lovingly from God, and bring them up according to the law of Christ and his Church?" ❧ "Since it is your intention to enter into marriage, join your right hands, and declare your consent before God and his Church."
Consent	❧ "I, N. _____, take you, N. _____ to be my wife/husband." ❧ "I promise to be true to you in good times and in bad, in sickness and in health." ❧ "I will love you and honor you all the days of my life." — Consent through questions — Recited after priest — Memorized
Reception of Consent	❧ "You have declared your consent before the Church. May the Lord in his goodness strengthen your consent and fill you both with his blessings. What God has joined, men must not divide." — May be accompanied with a musical acclamation by the assembly.
Blessing and Exchange of Rings	❧ "N. _____ take this ring as a sign of my love and fidelity. In the name of the Father, and of the Son, and of the Holy Spirit." — Three prayer options — Song/music after blessing of the rings — Double ring ceremony — Single ring ceremony
General Intercessions	— Three suggested forms — Personalization possible

THE CELEBRATION OF MARRIAGE

LITURGY OF THE EUCHARIST [*]

Recommended when both bride and groom are Catholic.

[*] If bride and groom are not both Catholic, the recommendation is that there would be no Liturgy of the Eucharist out of respect for the non-Catholic party (and presumably their family) who would not be receiving Holy Communion. If this is the case, the couple may choose to include the Lord's Prayer and Nuptial Blessing before continuing next with the Concluding Rites.

Preparation of the Gifts	◦ Two gift bearers ◦ Choice of music
Eucharistic Prayer	
The Lord's Prayer	
Nuptial Blessing	◦ Three options
Sign of Peace	◦ Couple only ◦ Couple to wedding party ◦ Couple to wedding party and parents ◦ Couple to wedding party
The Breaking of the Bread	
Communion	◦ Under both species ◦ Communion song/music
Prayer after Communion	

CONCLUDING RITES

Solemn Blessing	◦ Four options
Dismissal	
Recessional	◦ Many choices for music

Questions regarding intentions

❖ The questions regarding intentions are the same for all couples regardless of their religious affiliation.

❖ The questions regarding intentions determine that you:

— Freely and without reservation choose to give yourself to each other in marriage,

— Intend a life-long union,

— Are open to children and to raising them in the Catholic Church.

Exchange of consent

❖ The vows/consent are the same for all couples regardless of their religious affiliation.

❖ Despite which option you choose, it is beautiful to commit your vows to memory.

❖ We also recommend reflecting on your vows before your wedding day. This can make the exchange of vows even more meaningful on the day of your wedding.

❖ Remember: Your marriage comes about through your mutual consent.

RESOURCE

A Letter to All Engaged Couples from the Tribunal

Dear Engaged Couples:

As Tribunal Staff, specializing in matrimonial canon law, we work frequently with marriages that have failed. Based on our experience, we have found that in the majority of failed marriages areas of concern pre-exist the wedding. In order to have a good and successful marriage, couples need to identify serious issues before the wedding day.

It is common for engaged couples to have "jitters" before the wedding day. Sometimes, it is about the wedding arrangements, the ceremony, or the reception—these concerns are important, but not necessarily signs of potential difficulties. However, sometimes the worries are about more serious concerns, i.e., issues of fidelity, trust, or the existence of addictions.

Engagement is not a permanent commitment or marriage. Engagement is a mutual plan to work together toward marriage and to further evaluate if "we are meant for each other." Engagement does not necessarily have to end in a marriage. It is far wiser to postpone, or even end an engagement rather than to enter marriage with serious issues or reservations.

Our purpose in providing the following material is not to break up an engagement, but to make sure you enter marriage in true freedom and without the deck stacked against you. Now is the time to be working on making your future marriage the best it can be. We hope you will take the time to discuss any of these issues before your marriage.

- *Previous marriage.*
- *Addictions:* Substance use, gambling, pornography, etc.
- *Abuse:* Emotional, physical, or sexual abuse.
- *Significant psychological problems.*
- *Detrimental character traits:* Extreme jealousy, short or violent temper, compulsive behaviors, criminal behavior.
- *Attachments:* A dependency upon parents for emotional or financial support, continued attachment to prior boy/girlfriend.
- *Emotional instability:* History of many short term relationships or multiple previous partnerships.
- *Disapproval of others:* Concerns or hesitations expressed through this or a similar sentiment: "People who know me and matter to me have expressed doubts about the relationship."

❖ *Irrational thinking:* "No other man/woman is going to love me." "Marriage will change him/her." "I will be able to change him/her."

❖ *Issues of trust:* Concerns or hesitations expressed through these or similar sentiments: "I'm not able to trust him/her." "My fiancé/e's words or behavior hurt my trust in him/her." "I've lost trust in him/her."

❖ *Lack of freedom:* Concerns or hesitations expressed through these or similar sentiments: "I feel under pressure." "I have to follow through on my commitment even though I feel I shouldn't." "I am marrying to please others." "I cannot risk hurting him/her." "I have to do the right thing." "I'm afraid of what would happen if I don't go through with this." "I need to leave my family situation." "Marriage will solve my problems." "I have to prove to others that I'm responsible and can make my own decisions." "I am getting married because of pregnancy." "This is my only or last chance for marriage." "This is my only or last chance to have children." "I am the only son/daughter not married."

❖ *Readiness:* Concerns or hesitations expressed through these or similar sentiments: "I am not sure I really know him/her as well as I should." "I feel we do not have enough time to get to know each other." "I haven't had a chance to know his/her family." "I do not know enough about his/her history." "I feel I got engaged too soon." "It seems like it is just the next logical step."

❖ *Relational issues:* Concerns or hesitations expressed through these or similar sentiments: "I feel I am not able to express my feelings to him/her." "I'm not able to totally be myself in the relationship." "I feel inferior to him/her." "He/she makes important decisions without consulting me." "We can't make decisions together without arguing." "He/she does not take my feelings seriously." "It seems that his/her only interest is sex." "I feel he/she is not affectionate toward me."

❖ *Spiritual/moral differences:* Concerns or hesitations expressed through these or similar sentiments: "We have very different moral and religious values." "Our spiritual differences are causing strife in our relationship and/or family."

❖ *Disparate values and goals:* Concerns or hesitations expressed through these or similar sentiments: "We disagree on some key values." "We have separate goals." "We have conflicting attitudes toward money." "We never talk about our goals."

❖ *Family and marriage expectations:* Concerns or hesitations expressed through these or similar sentiments: "We disagree on husband/wife roles." "We disagree about having children or their education and religious identity." "Our expectations of working in/outside the home differ."

If you have concerns, it may be extremely difficult to bring them up. Do not be afraid, have courage. If you address concerns now, you may save yourself and your fiancé/e future pain. If you have trouble coming to a resolution, you may benefit from speaking with a priest, deacon, or a professional counselor or therapist. Often couples can resolve these issues and therefore feel confident going forward with marriage.

In our culture of divorce, it can be easy to slip into thinking, "If this marriage does not work out, I can always try again." This thinking is opposed to our Catholic belief in the permanence of marriage. Therefore, you should enter this marriage believing that this is your one chance to make this lifelong commitment.

You still have time to work toward this goal by addressing any serious concerns now, before your wedding (even if you are getting married very soon).

The Catholic Church wants strong, happy, and lifelong marriages. Trusting you will use this information to strengthen your relationship, we assure you of our prayers for your future.

Sincerely,

Staff from The Metropolitan Tribunal
of the Archdiocese of Boston

ACTIVITY
AM I PREPARED FOR A MARITAL COMMITMENT?

Directions: After reading the letter from the tribunal, identify any issues, concerns, or reservations you may have as you contemplate marriage. This exercise needs to be done with sincerity and honesty.

Previous marriage: _____

Addictions: _____

Abuse: _____

Significant psychological problems: _____

Detrimental character traits: _____

Attachments: _____

Emotional instability: _____

Disapproval of others: _____

Irrational thinking: _____

Issues of trust: _____

Lack of freedom: _____

Readiness: _____

Relational issues: _____

Spiritual/moral differences: _____

Disparate values and goals: _____

Family and marriage expectations: _____

It is important that any issues, concerns, or reservations be discussed with your fiancé/e in an atmosphere of trust and love. You may benefit from speaking with a priest, deacon, or professional counselor. Contact your local diocesan Marriage and Family Life Office for more assistance.

DATE NIGHT ACTIVITY

Directions: Compose a love letter to your fiancé/e. What are your hopes, dreams, and aspirations for your marriage? Base your sentiments on any of the elements of Catholic marriage and/or marital love. To aid reflection, review pages 51–52.

You can exchange your letters:

* after the wedding rehearsal, to be read in preparation for the wedding celebration;
* after the wedding celebration, as part of your private celebration of the day;
* during your honeymoon;
* whenever you would like.

Dear _____

_____

_____

_____

_____

_____

_____

_____

_____

_____

_____

_____

_____

_____

Love, _____

OPTIONS FOR SCRIPTURE READINGS
DURING A CATHOLIC WEDDING

First Reading (Old Testament)

1. Male and female he created them (Genesis 1:26–28, 31a).

2. The two of them become one body (Genesis 2:18–24).

3. In his love for Rebekah, Isaac found solace after the death of his mother (Genesis 24:48–51, 58–67).

4. May the Lord of heaven prosper you both. May he grant you mercy and peace (Tobit 7:6–14).

5. Allow us to live together to a happy old age (Tobit 8:4b–8).

6. The woman who fears the Lord is to be praised (Proverbs 31:10–13, 19–20, 30–31).

7. Stern as death is love (Song of Songs 2:8–10, 14, 16a; 8:6–7a).

8. Like the sun rising in the Lord's heavens, the beauty of a virtuous wife is the radiance of her home (Sirach 26:1–4, 13–16).

9. I will make a new covenant with the house of Israel and the house of Judah (Jeremiah 31:31–32a, 33–34a).

Responsorial Psalm

The following list is the text of the assembly's response.

1. The earth is full of the goodness of the Lord (Psalm 33:12 and 18, 20–21, 22).

2. I will bless the Lord at all times (Psalm 34:2–3, 4–5, 6–7, 8–9).

3. The Lord is kind and merciful (Psalm 103:1–2, 8 and 13, 17–18a).

4. Blessed the man who greatly delights in the Lord's commands (Psalm 112:1bc–2, 3–4, 5–7a, 7b–8, 9).

5. Blessed are those who fear the Lord (Psalm 128:1–2, 3, 4–5).

6. The Lord is compassionate toward all his works (Psalm 145:8–9, 10 and 15, 17–18).

7. Let all praise the name of the Lord (Psalm 148:1–2, 3–4, 9–10, 11–13a, 13c–14a).

Second Reading (New Testament)

1. What will separate us from the love of Christ? (Romans 8:31b–35, 37–39).

2. Offer your bodies as a living sacrifice, holy and pleasing to God (Romans 12:1–2, 9–18 [long form], or Romans 12:1–2, 9–13 [short form]).

3. Welcome one another as Christ welcomed you (Romans 15:1b–3a, 5–7, 13).

4. Your body is a temple of the Spirit. Your bodies are members of the Body of Christ (1 Corinthians 6:13c–15a, 17–20).

5. If I do not have love, I gain nothing (1 Corinthians 12:31–13:8a).

6. This is a great mystery, but I speak in reference to Christ and the Church (Ephesians 5:2a, 21–33 [long form], or Ephesians 5:2a, 25–32 [short form]).

7. The God of peace will be with you (Philippians 4:4–9).

8. And over all these put on love, that is, the bond of perfection (Colossians 3:12–17).

9. Let marriage be held in honor by all (Hebrews 13:1–4a, 5–6b).

10. Be of one mind, sympathetic, loving toward one another (1 Peter 3:1–9).

11. Love in deed and in truth (1 John 3:18–24).

12. God is love (1 John 4:7–12).

13. Blessed are those who have been called to the wedding feast of the Lamb (Revelation 19:1, 5–9a).

Gospel

1. Rejoice and be glad, for your reward will be great in heaven (Matthew 5:1–12a).

2. You are the light of the world (Matthew 5:13–16).

3. A wise man built his house on rock (Matthew 7:21, 24–29 [long form], or Matthew 7:21, 24–25 [short form]).

4. What God has united, man must not separate (Matthew 19:3–6).

5. This is the greatest and the first commandment. The second is like it (Matthew 22:35–40).

6. They are no longer two, but one flesh (Mark 10:6–9).

7. Jesus did this as the beginning of his signs in Cana in Galilee (John 2:1–11).

8. Remain in my love (John 15:9–12).

9. This is my commandment: love one another (John 15:12–16).

10. That they may be brought to perfection as one (John 17:20–26 [long form], or 17:20–23 [short form]).

OUR PREPARATION WORKSHEET FOR MARRIAGE WITHIN MASS

	OPTIONS	OUR CHOICE
Entrance Rites		
Gathering		
Welcome of Bride and Groom	At the door of the church or at the altar	
Procession	Both bride and groom accompanied by parents, preceded by ushers, bridesmaids, and presiding clergy	
	Both bride and groom accompanied by parents, preceded by ushers and bridesmaids	
	Bride accompanied by parents, preceded by ushers and bridesmaids	
	Bride accompanied by father, preceded by ushers and bridesmaids	
	Many choices for the entrance song	
Greeting		
Penitential Act		
Opening Prayer (Collect)		
Liturgy of the Word		
Old Testament Reading	Nine options	
	Choice of reader	
Responsorial Psalm	Seven options	
	Choice of reader/cantor	
	Choice of many musical settings	
New Testament Reading	Thirteen options	
	Choice of reader	
Gospel Acclamation	Choice of musical settings	
Gospel	Ten options (proclaimed by deacon or priest)	
Homily	Based on the Scriptures, Church teaching on marriage, and the couple's lives	

Rite of Marriage

Address to the Couple

Questions Regarding Intentions

Consent	Consent through questions	
	Recited after priest	
	Memorized	
Reception of Consent	May be accompanied with a musical acclamation by the assembly	
Blessing and Exchange of Rings	Three prayer options	
	Song/music after blessing of the rings	
	Double ring ceremony	
	Single ring ceremony	
General Intercessions	Three suggested forms	
	Personalization possible	

Liturgy of the Eucharist

Presentation and Preparation of the Gifts	Two gift bearers	
	Choice of music	

Eucharistic Prayer

The Lord's Prayer

Nuptial Blessing	Three options	
Sign of Peace	Couple only	
	Couple to wedding party	
	Couple to wedding party and parents	

Lamb of God

Communion	Under both species	
	Communion song/music	

Prayer after Communion

Concluding Rites

Solemn Blessing	Four options	

Dismissal

Recessional	Many choices for music	

OUR PREPARATION WORKSHEET
FOR MARRIAGE OUTSIDE OF MASS

	OPTIONS	OUR CHOICE
Entrance Rites		
Gathering		
Welcome of Bride and Groom	At the door of the church or at the altar	
Procession	Both bride and groom accompanied by parents, preceded by ushers, bridesmaids, and presiding clergy	
	Both bride and groom accompanied by parents, preceded by ushers and bridesmaids	
	Bride accompanied by parents, preceded by ushers and bridesmaids	
	Bride accompanied by father, preceded by ushers and bridesmaids	
	Many choices for the entrance song	
Greeting		
Opening Prayer		
Liturgy of the Word		
Old Testament Reading	Nine options	
	Choice of reader	
Responsorial Psalm	Seven options	
	Choice of reader/cantor	
	Choice of many musical settings	
New Testament Reading	Thirteen options	
	Choice of reader	
Gospel Acclamation	Choice of musical settings	
Gospel	Ten options (proclaimed by deacon or priest)	
Homily	Based on the Scriptures, Church teachings on marriage, and the couple's lives.	

Rite of Marriage

Address to the Couple		
Questions Regarding Intentions		
Consent	Consent through questions	
	Recited after priest	
	Memorized	
Reception of Consent	May be accompanied with a musical acclamation by the assembly	
Blessing and Exchange of Rings	Three prayer options	
	Song/music after blessing of the rings	
	Double ring ceremony	
	Single ring ceremony	
General Intercessions	Three suggested forms	
	Personalization possible	
Nuptial Blessing	Three options	
	May be omitted	

Concluding Rites

Lord's Prayer	May be omitted	
Solemn Blessing	Four options	
Dismissal		
Recessional	Many choices for music	

EXHORTATION TO COUPLES

My dear friends: You are about to enter into a union which is most sacred and most serious. It is most sacred, because established by God himself; most serious, because it will bind you together for life in a relationship so close and so intimate that it will profoundly influence your whole future.

That future, with its hopes and disappointments, its successes and its failures, its pleasures and its pains, its joys and its sorrows, is hidden from your eyes. You know that these elements are mingled in every life, and are to be expected in your own. And so not knowing what is before you, you take each other for better or for worse, for richer or for poorer, in sickness and in health, until death.

Truly, then, these words are most serious. It is a beautiful tribute to your undoubted faith in each other, that recognizing their full import, you are nevertheless so willing and ready to pronounce them. And because these words involve such solemn obligations, it is most fitting that you rest the security of your wedded life upon the great principle of self-sacrifice.

And so you begin your married life by the voluntary and complete surrender of your individual lives in the interest of that deeper and wider life which you are to have in common. Henceforth you will belong entirely to each other; you will be one in mind, one in heart, and one in affections. And whatever sacrifices you may hereafter be required to make to preserve this mutual life, always make them generously.

Sacrifice is usually difficult and irksome. Only love can make it easy, and perfect love can make it a joy. We are willing to give in proportion as we love. And when love is perfect the sacrifice is complete. God so loved the world that he gave his only-begotten Son, and the Son so loved us that he gave himself for our salvation. Greater love than this no man has, that a man lay down his life for his friends.

No greater blessing can come to your married life than pure conjugal love, loyal and true to the end. May, then, this love with which you join your hands and hearts today, never fail, but grow deeper and stronger as the years go on. And if true love and the unselfish spirit of perfect sacrifice guide your every action, you can expect the greatest measure of earthly happiness that may be allotted to man in this vale of tears.

The rest is in the hands of God. Nor will God be wanting to your needs; he will pledge you the life-long support of his graces in the holy sacrament that you now receive.[1]

---

1. From the 1964 Roman Rite of Catholic Marriage.

PERSONAL NOTES

Finances

Yours, Mine, OURS:
Resources for Marriage
and Family Life

"For where your treasure is,
there also will your heart be."
MATTHEW 6:21

HOUSE METAPHOR

ശ In order to rent, buy, or build a house, we need financial resources.

ശ As Christians, you will want to be good stewards of your financial resources and develop a unified Christian approach.

GOALS OF THIS TOPIC

ശ *Be wise*: To help you evaluate your own attitudes toward finances and share those with each other.

ശ *Be skilled* and be *faithful*: To help you develop a unified Christian approach to managing finances that is responsible and generous.

Attitudes about money are shaped by

❖ Family of origin

❖ Temperament

❖ Culture

How do I feel about money?

❖ Main focus

❖ Scared of it

❖ It grows on trees

❖ Indifferent

How do I approach finances?

❖ Saver

❖ Spender

❖ Thrifty

❖ Competitor

Why do I go shopping?

❖ Necessity

❖ Recreation

❖ Therapy

Financial expectations

- ❖ Financial roles and responsibilities
- ❖ Saving/spending patterns
- ❖ Salaries/earning potential
- ❖ Accumulation/payment of debt
- ❖ Home ownership
- ❖ Retirement savings
- ❖ College savings for children

Conflict over money

- ❖ Similar views—no balance
- ❖ Different views—abundant conflict
- ❖ Unmet or unrealistic expectations
- ❖ Underlying issues

Four Christian Values

1. Gratitude
   - ❖ Be grateful to God for all we have.
   - ❖ Everything we have—our time, talents, and treasure—comes from God.

2. Trust
   - ❖ God will provide for our needs.
   - ❖ Jesus taught us to trust God, "Give us this day our daily bread."
   - ❖ All of our American money says, "In God we trust."

3. Stewardship
   - ❖ All good things that God has given us are meant to be shared.
   - ❖ We should see money as given to us by God to be used not only for our own purposes but for his purposes.
   - ❖ A biblical instruction for stewardship is "tithing," which is 10 percent of our time, talent, and treasure. This may be a good goal to aim for.

4. Detachment
   - ❖ Keep money in its rightful place.
   - ❖ Money is important—we need it to live and it can do much good—but be clear about keeping it in perspective. See it for what it is and don't be too attached to it.

Five Financial Recommendations

1. Be honest.

    ❖ Become aware of your own attitudes, values, and knowledge concerning money.

    ❖ Share these with each other.

    ❖ Use TLC to help you talk about financial matters.

    ❖ Disclose current financial status: debts, obligations, savings, etc.

    ❖ Full disclosure is important as you begin your marriage.

2. Be a team.

    ❖ Remember: Marriage is a partnership of the whole of life (this includes financial matters). In marriage, each person's financial assets and liabilities become the other's.

    ❖ Combine revenue and expenses.

    ❖ Decision-making should be shared.

    ❖ Utilize individual strengths.

    ❖ Help one another in areas of individual weakness.

3. Be informed.

    ❖ Pursue continuing education: What do you need to learn?

    ❖ If necessary, seek outside advice: consult a financial planner to address short-term and long-term goals.

    ❖ Sometimes a neutral outside party can be very helpful.

    ❖ Find someone you trust, preferably someone with similar financial values.

4. Be generous and responsible.

    ❖ Be generous: Remember the principles of stewardship. Consider how you can help others financially. Develop a spirit of generosity.

    ❖ Be responsible: Usually when couples are irresponsible with money it is not because they are too generous, but because they do not control spending.

    ❖ Make a spending and savings plan.

    ❖ Discuss appropriate use of credit.

    ❖ Distinguish needs vs. wants.

5. Be steadfast.

  ❖ Stay firm in purpose.

  ❖ If bad habits take over, get back on course.

  ❖ Watch for signals of being off course: increasing debt, lack of awareness of financial status and goals, lack of generosity, lack of responsibility, lack of unified approach.

Conclusion

  ✓ Be aware of your financial attitudes, behaviors, and expectations.

  ✓ Integrate the four Christian values and five financial recommendations into your marriage.

  ✓ Use TLC and the five steps to managing expectations to develop a financial action plan.

ACTIVITY
FINANCIAL EXPECTATIONS

Directions: Answer these questions individually and then share your answers with your fiancé/e.

1. Identify your approach to money and your main reasons for shopping:

Approach to money	Me	Future Spouse
Saver		
Spender		
Thrifty		
Competitor		
Other:		

Reasons for shopping	Me	Future Spouse
Necessity		
Recreation		
Therapy		
Other:		

2. What are my attitudes concerning money?

3. Where do they come from?

4. What expectations do I have regarding financial roles and responsibilities?

Saving/spending patterns:

_____

Salaries/earning potential:

_____

Accumulation/payment of debt:

_____

Home ownership:

_____

Retirement savings:

_____

College savings for children:

_____

5. Do you integrate these Christian values in your financial matters? Would you like to?

Christian Value	Yes	Would like to
Gratitude		
Trust		
Stewardship		
Detachment		

6. Do you incorporate these recommendations in your financial matters? Would you like to?

Recommendation	Yes	Would like to
Be honest		
Be a team		
Be informed		
Be generous and responsible		
Be steadfast		

7. What is one financial strength you see in yourself?

8. What is one financial strength you see in your future spouse?

9. Is there any important financial information I have not disclosed to my fiancé/e (e.g., student loans, consumer debt)?

10. How do I feel about sharing finances in marriage?

11. How will we share our resources with the Church and those in need?

12. What are my financial goals?

13. What are my biggest financial concerns?

14. What could be potential conflicts?

15. What steps do we need to take immediately in regard to financial matters?

OUR FINANCIAL CONDITION   Date: _____

Assets (What we own)	His	Hers	Ours
CURRENT ASSETS			
Cash (checking account)			
Cash (savings, money markets, CD's)			
Personal property-market value (auto, jewelry, etc.)			
Total current assets			
LONG-TERM ASSETS			
Certificates of deposit			
Debt owed to you			
Life insurance (cash values)			
Real estate (net market value)			
Other real estate			
Retirement accounts			
Securities (stocks, bonds, mutual funds, etc.)			
Other (itemize)			
Total long-term assets			
TOTAL ASSETS			

OUR FINANCIAL CONDITION   Date: _____

Liabilities (What we owe)	His	Hers	Ours
CURRENT LIABILITIES			
Charge accounts			
Credit cards			
Current monthly unpaid bills			
Personal debts (short-term)			
Unpaid taxes and interest			
Unsecured loans (short-term)			
Other short-term debts (itemize)			
Total current liabilities			
LONG-TERM LIABILITIES			
Mortgages			
Home equity loans			
Student loans			
Car loans			
Notes cosigned, etc.			
Other loans (itemize)			
Taxes (we owe)			
Other long-term liabilities (itemize)			
Total long-term liabilities			
TOTAL LIABILITIES			
Net Worth (Total assets less total liabilities)			

OUR SPENDING PLAN	Date: _____				
	Monthly Plan	Yearly Plan	Monthly Actual	Yearly Actual	Difference (+ or -)
INCOME					
Net					
Interest					
Other					
INCOME TOTAL					
EXPENSES					
Savings					
Emergency fund					
Retirement fund					
College fund					
Investment fund					
Vacation fund					
Other					
Total					
Debt Repayment					
Student loans					
Home equity loans					
Credit cards					
Other					
Total					
Stewardship					
Faith community					
Other					
Total					
Housing					
Mortgage/rent					
Real estate taxes					
Insurance					

OUR SPENDING PLAN

	Monthly Plan	Yearly Plan	Monthly Actual	Yearly Actual	Difference (+ or -)
Gas/oil					
Electricity					
Heat					
Water and sewer					
Phone-landline					
Internet service					
Cable TV/satellite					
Garbage/sanitation					
Home maintenance and repairs					
Other					
Total					
Food					
Groceries					
Eating out					
Other					
Total					
Transportation					
Auto loan/lease payment					
Auto insurance					
Gas					
Car maintenance and repairs					
Tolls					
Public transit					
Other					
Total					
Insurance					
Life					
Medical/dental					
Total					

OUR SPENDING PLAN

	Monthly Plan	Yearly Plan	Monthly Actual	Yearly Actual	Difference (+ or -)
Entertainment					
Movies					
Books					
Outings					
Vacations					
Other					
Total					
Personal					
Cell phone					
Clothing					
Gifts					
Subscriptions					
Medical/Dental					
Dry cleaning					
Haircut/beauty					
Other					
Total					
Miscellaneous					
Miscellaneous 1					
Miscellaneous 2					
Miscellaneous 3					
Total					
EXPENSES TOTAL					
INCOME LESS EXPENSES					

WEDDING SPENDING:
WHAT DOES THE CATHOLIC CHURCH SAY?

Budgeting for Your Wedding

Costs vary by region, but the average wedding ranges between $20,000 and $25,000. Some couples justify their spending because it's a "once in a lifetime" event. Others feel pressured by families and friends to stage an elaborate celebration. Expectations may be greater for couples who have been on their own for a while. Presumably, they have more financial resources, plus they've accumulated lots of great ideas from their friends' weddings.

The Catholic Church understands a couple's desire for an appropriate celebration of their marriage with family and friends. In the Catholic Church, marriage is a sacrament. All sacraments are to be celebrated because they are encounters with Jesus Christ. A wedding celebrates Christ's gift of marital love to this particular man and woman. It is a time for rejoicing.

But what is "appropriate"? The U.S. Catholic bishops have not spoken directly about wedding spending, but couples might ask the following questions before setting up a wedding budget.

Couples frequently say they want their wedding to express who they are. Of course, a Christian wedding is much more than a personal identity statement. Still, this is a legitimate concern; after all, the wedding is the couple's first public act as husband and wife. It should say something about what's important to them. Do you want to express hospitality, gratitude for the support of family and friends, and a commitment to share your love with others? Then plan a wedding that highlights those values.

According to a national study, debt brought into marriage is among the top three problematic issues for newly married couples. Many couples are already struggling with credit card debt and student loans. Do you really want to add wedding debt to the mix? Financial worries can strain even seasoned couples. Newly married couples are especially at risk.

You may have heard the Engaged Encounter slogan: "A wedding is a day, a marriage is a lifetime." In other words, what are your priorities? The engagement period is not only a time to plan the wedding, but to prepare for your married lives. Too much concentration on the former can take time from the must-have conversations that need to take place before the wedding. It can also turn you into an overstressed Bride- or Groomzilla.

The U.S. bishops have called people to "carefully consider our choices and lifestyles." They point out that "we live in a culture that prizes the consumption of material goods. While the poor often have too little, many of us can be easily caught up in a frenzy of wanting more and more" (Global Climate Change, 15).

Moderation is the key. If you have a feeling that wedding expenses are getting out of hand, they probably are. To restore your focus, consider how your wedding might express your concern for the needy. Some couples prepare a large food basket that they bring forward along with the bread and wine for Mass. Other couples include a request on their wedding invitations that guests bring one or two items of non-perishable food to the church. These are then given to the parish food pantry or a local food bank. Couples can also make a donation, from the money they may receive as gifts, to the parish's social outreach committee.

Can you really cut down on wedding expenses? Absolutely![1]

1. United States Conference of Catholic Bishops, "Planning a Catholic Wedding: Budgeting for Your Wedding" accessed on May 1, 2012 at http://foryourmarriage.org/catholic-marriage/planning-a-catholic-wedding/spending/.

Eight Spiritual Practices for Marriage and Family Life

Nurturing Faith: Building a Firm Foundation

"I will show you what someone is like who comes to me, listens to my words, and acts on them. That one is like a person building a house, who dug deeply and laid the foundation on rock; when the flood came, the river burst against that house but could not shake it because it had been well built."

Luke 6:47–48

HOUSE METAPHOR

෨ Just as a house needs a firm foundation, so too does marriage need a firm foundation.

෨ We proprose that faith be your foundation.

GOALS OF THIS TOPIC

෨ *Be wise* and *be true*: To propose a way to keep first things first and set priorities within marriage.

෨ *Be wise, be skilled,* and *be faithful*: To provide practical information regarding eight spiritual practices that nurture faith and build a strong foundation for marriage and family life.

Setting priorities

❖ To be transformed in love and to build a Catholic marriage and family you need a solid foundation.

❖ We propose this solid foundation is faith and a relationship with God.

❖ We have to "keep first things first."

❖ Our relationship with God is our most important relationship, our number one priority.

❖ Our nuclear family relationship, in its totality, is next in importance after our relationship with God.

❖ Marital love, as the core of the family, becomes embodied in children.

Eight important spiritual practices for marriage and family

❖ You may already do a few or all of these practices.

❖ If you are new to spiritual practices, start small and pick one practice.

❖ Don't be overwhelmed and don't give up!

❖ God wants each of us to grow closer to him and be transformed in love.

❖ God is already active in your life. He brought you here today and has given you your future spouse.

Spiritual Practice 1: Pray.

❖ Prayer is speaking and listening to God

❖ Just as in human communication we need TLC, we also need to talk to God, listen to God, and check in with him.

❖ Pray for your spouse, your marriage, and your children.

❖ No one knows him or her better—so who better to pray for him or her!

❖ You can pray for his or her dreams and needs, for God to work in a special way in his or her life.

❖ Pray as a couple and as a family.

Suggestions:

— If you do pray, continue.

— If you don't pray, start.

— You can find prayers and resources at the end of this chapter (p. 95).

Spiritual Practice 2: Be attentive to the voice and action of God.

❖ God has a specific plan for our lives and he cares about all the details of our lives.

❖ We can know his plan, wishes, and desires for us by being attentive to his voice and action in our daily lives.

❖ God speaks to us through many things including:

— Scripture;

— The teachings of the Church;

— Other people (particularly people who are wiser and more advanced in the spiritual life);

— Prayer;

— Circumstances in our lives;

— Opportunities that present themselves and avenues that are not open to us;

— Our conscience;

— The desires of our heart;

— Our natural abilities and interests;

— Sense of internal peace.

Suggestions:

— Pay attention to the "coincidences in life."

— Periodically, reflect on your interactions with others, the events in your life, and your marriage.

— Consider finding a spiritual director, someone who is trained to help others listen to God.

— Pray and listen to God.

Spiritual Practice 3: Participate in spiritual enrichment and formation.

❖ To live an adult Christian life we need to have an adult understanding and experience of Christian faith.

❖ For many of us, spiritual formation stops in high school.

❖ We need to continue to learn more about our faith.

Suggestions:

— If you participate in spiritual enrichment, continue and perhaps add a new experience.

— If you don't participate in spiritual enrichment, begin.

— There are many ways to participate in adult spiritual enrichment:

> Books, i.e., Bible, biographies of saints
>
> Courses
>
> Conferences
>
> Workshops/seminars
>
> Retreats
>
> Parish missions or lectures
>
> Catholic magazines, newspapers, radio stations, TV channels, Websites, etc.
>
> Catholic movies/DVDs
>
> Bible study groups
>
> CDs

Spiritual Practice 4: Practice repentance.

AS A COUPLE AND FAMILY:

❖ Practicing repentance is important in all our relationships and vital for a healthy marriage and family.

❖ In marriage and family, on many occasions we will need to apologize, ask forgiveness, and seek to make amends.

❖ When children see parents practicing repentance and offering forgiveness it teaches them that although sin is real, forgiveness and reconciliation are stronger.

❖ These three sentences are a powerful way to apologize:

> *"I'm sorry."* It is important to say "I'm sorry." It shows sorrow for and ownership of the wrong done.
>
> *"Please forgive me."* This sentence expresses the desire on your part to receive forgiveness.
>
> *"What can I do to make amends?"* This shows you want to make things right.

WITH GOD:

❖ What is true in human relationships is also true in our relationship with God.

❖ In order to have a strong relationship with God, we need to turn away from things in our lives that undermine this relationship and our ability to love.

❖ Sin damages our relationship with God and our ability to love properly.

❖ As Catholics we have the sacrament of Confession or Reconciliation, an opportunity to say to God:

> *"I'm sorry."*
>
> *"Please forgive me."*
>
> *"What can I do to make amends?"*

❖ The sacrament deals with a past wrong, but also heals our present relationship with God and strengthens us for the future.

❖ God is eager to forgive *every* sin.

❖ In Confession, through the priest, Jesus forgives our sins, our relationship with God the Father is strengthened through Jesus in the Holy Spirit, and we receive the gracious help of Jesus to do better.

❖ The forgiveness offered in the sacrament is absolute. As far as God is concerned, the sins no longer exist and no judgment or condemnation remains.

Suggestions:

— Go to Confession before your wedding day to begin your life together with a fresh start.

— There is a confession guide in this workbook (p. 100).

— Do not be afraid! Look forward to the peace you will feel afterward.

Spiritual Practice 5: Spend time with faith-filled friends.

❖ Faith-filled friends support us and provide encouragement in living the Christian life.

❖ They help us mature spiritually as we learn from them and they learn from us.

Suggestions:

— Find and spend time with others who will support you in the faith.

— Your faith will grow if you are mentored or if you mentor others in the faith.

Spiritual Practice 6: Be an active member of a parish.

❖ Being an active member of a parish identifies us as a disciple of Christ.

❖ It gives us support and encouragement in living the Christian life.

❖ It moves us out of isolation and gives us opportunities to share faith and faith experiences.

❖ It helps us mature spiritually as we learn from others and they learn from us.

❖ It enables us to participate in Christ's work in the world and to serve others.

❖ It keeps us on track and allows us to help others keep on track.

Suggestions:

— Join a parish and become an active member of the parish.

— Use your gifts to serve the Church in whatever areas you feel able.

— The Church needs you!

Spiritual Practice 7: Share God's love with others.

❖ Each of us has a unique way of sharing God's love with others.

❖ In the Catholic Church we have identified works of service or mercy that provide for the physical, emotional, and/or spiritual needs of others.

❖ They are called the corporal and spiritual works of mercy.

❖ Parents do many of these all the time: feed the hungry, counsel the doubtful, etc.

❖ We should seek to do them all, but each of us may feel drawn to particular works.

Suggestions:

THE SEVEN CORPORAL WORKS OF MERCY	THE SEVEN SPIRITUAL WORKS OF MERCY
1. Feed the hungry.	1. Counsel the doubtful.
2. Give drink to the thirsty.	2. Instruct the ignorant.
3. Clothe the naked.	3. Admonish sinners.
4. Shelter the homeless.	4. Comfort the afflicted.
5. Visit the sick.	5. Forgive offenses.
6. Visit the imprisoned.	6. Bear wrongs patiently.
7. Bury the dead.	7. Pray for the living and the dead.

Spiritual Practice 8: Participate in the Mass.

❖ The Mass is the central and most sacred act of Catholic worship.

❖ There are many reasons we go to Mass.

❖ As Catholic disciples of Christ, it is our obligation and our privilege to attend Mass on the Lord's Day and holy days of obligation.

Suggestions:

— Attend weekly Mass and consider attending more often.

— Prepare for and actively participate in Mass (see Topic 10 for more on this).

RESOURCES FOR SPIRITUAL GROWTH

One of the best ways to develop our relationship with God is to spend time with him in prayer.

Tips for praying

❖ Find a regular time to pray each day. This will help prayer become part of your daily routine.

❖ Find a quiet place and remove distractions. Prayer can be done anywhere but it is best to have a quiet location that is conducive to focusing our attention on God.

❖ Use formal prayers (see below) or speak to God from your heart, or use a combination of both. It is important to note that there is no "right" way to pray. Experiment with different styles and forms of prayer.

❖ Take time to listen. God does speak to us in prayer but we need to listen with our hearts, to pay attention. Perhaps he will speak to you through your feelings, new insights, or stirrings in your heart.

❖ Read something to help inspire and guide your prayer, i.e., the Bible, spiritual writings, daily Mass readings, devotional books.

❖ Keep a prayer journal where you can note insights, prayers requested and answered, feelings, inspirations, etc.

Traditional Prayers

Morning Offering

God, our Father, I offer you today all that I think and do and say. I offer it with what was done on earth by Jesus Christ, your Son. Amen.

Prayer Before Meals

Bless us, O Lord, and these thy gifts, which we are about to receive from thy bounty, through Christ our Lord. Amen.

Prayer After Meals

We give you thanks, Almighty God, for all your benefits. And may the souls of the faithful departed, through the mercy of God, rest in peace. Amen.

Prayer at the End of the Day

God, our Father, this day is done. We ask you and Jesus Christ, your Son, that with the Spirit, our welcome guest, you guard our sleep and bless our rest. Amen.

Sign of the Cross

(Can be done at any time but especially when beginning and ending prayers, passing a church, or when genuflecting in front of a tabernacle.)

In the name of the Father, and of the Son, and of the Holy Spirit. Amen.

Our Father

Our Father who art in heaven, hallowed be thy name; thy kingdom come, thy will be done on earth as it is in heaven. Give us this day our daily bread, and forgive us our trespasses, as we forgive those who trespass against us. And lead us not into temptation, but deliver us from evil. Amen.

Hail Mary

Hail Mary, full of grace, the Lord is with you. Blessed are you among women and blessed is the fruit of your womb, Jesus. Holy Mary, Mother of God, pray for us sinners, now and at the hour of our death. Amen.

Glory Be

Glory be to the Father, and to the Son, and to the Holy Spirit. As it was in the beginning, is now, and ever shall be, world without end. Amen.

Prayer to Your Guardian Angel

Angel of God, my guardian dear, to whom God's love commits me here, ever this day/night, be at my side, to light and guard, to rule and guide. Amen.

Memorare

Remember, O most gracious Virgin Mary, that never was it known that anyone who fled to your protection, implored your help, or sought your intercession was left unaided. Inspired by this confidence, I fly to you, O Virgin of virgins, my Mother; to you I come, before you I stand, sinful and sorrowful. O Mother of the Word Incarnate, despise not my petitions, but in your mercy hear and answer me. Amen.

Act of Faith, Hope, and Love

Jesus, I believe in you. Jesus, I hope in you. Jesus, I love you.

Serenity Prayer

God, grant me the serenity to accept the things I cannot change, the courage to change the things I can, and the wisdom to know the difference. Living one day at a time, enjoying one moment at a time, accepting hardship as a pathway to peace. Taking, as Jesus did, this sinful world as it is, not as I would have it. Trusting that you will make all things right if I surrender to your will. So that I may be reasonably happy in this life and supremely happy with you forever in the next. Amen. (Reinhold Niebuhr)

Nicene Creed

I believe in one God, the Father almighty, maker of heaven and earth, of all things visible and invisible.

I believe in one Lord Jesus Christ, the Only Begotten Son of God, born of the Father before all ages. God from God, Light from Light, true God from true God, begotten, not made, consubstantial with the Father; through him all things were made.

For us men and for our salvation he came down from heaven, and by the Holy Spirit was incarnate of the Virgin Mary, and became man. For our sake he was crucified under Pontius Pilate, he suffered death and was buried, and rose again on the third day in accordance with the Scriptures.

He ascended into heaven and is seated at the right hand of the Father. He will come again in glory to judge the living and the dead and his kingdom will have no end.

I believe in the Holy Spirit, the Lord, the giver of life, who proceeds from the Father and the Son, who with the Father and the Son is adored and glorified, who has spoken through the prophets.

I believe in one, holy, catholic and apostolic Church. I confess one Baptism for the forgiveness of sins and I look forward to the resurrection of the dead and the life of the world to come. Amen.

Spiritual Practices

Reading the Bible

Reading the Bible is a great way to grow in faith, know God better, and hear him speak to us through Scripture. The Bible is God's Word and is accessible to all of us. A good place to begin is to read one of the Gospels (Matthew, Mark, Luke, John). These are the books that record the life and teachings of Jesus.

Consider joining a Catholic Bible study group, possibly affiliated with a parish. There are many good Catholic resources for reading and studying the Bible that can be found at a local Catholic bookstore.

Prayerful reading *(Lectio Divina)*

This is usually done with the Bible but may be done with other devotional writings.

- ❖ Find a quiet place.
- ❖ Ask the Holy Spirit to bless your reading.

1. Read the passage slowly. When you finish, return to any word, phrase, sentence, or idea that struck you while reading.

    - ❖ Ask yourself: What struck me most while reading the passage?

2. Think about the word, phrase, sentence, or idea that struck you. Ask yourself:

    - ❖ Why this?
    - ❖ Might it be addressing something in my life?
    - ❖ Where does it touch my life today?
    - ❖ What does the Lord want me to learn from this?
    - ❖ What might God want me to do in response to this?

3. Speak/pray to God about the thoughts, ideas, and plans that have surfaced from this reflection time.

4. Rest in God's presence with an open mind and heart. Listen for God's response.

    - ❖ Ask yourself: What is God's response to me?
    - ❖ Don't force this part of the reflection. God often speaks to us outside the time of prayer.
    - ❖ Listening for God's response begins in prayer and continues subconsciously afterward.

Visiting the Lord in church or during Eucharistic Adoration

(Eucharistic Adoration is when the consecrated host is displayed in a special holder called a monstrance.)

- ❖ Make a short visit to pray and spend some time with Jesus.
- ❖ Schedule more frequent visits by committing to times set aside for Eucharistic Adoration in your parish or local church.

The examen prayer

- ❖ This prayer is generally done at the end of the day or week to help us reflect on our lives, actions, and the workings of God in our lives. The steps can easily be remembered by G-R-A-C-E.

STEP ONE: Gratitude for something in your life, past, present, or future.

STEP TWO: Request for insight to look at yourself honestly as God sees you.

STEP THREE: Accounting of your actions and attitude.

- ❖ Review your life since your last examen, looking at actions and attitudes, noting patterns and habits.

STEP FOUR: Chart your course.

- ❖ Are you on course? What needs changing or correcting? Contrition? Confession?

STEP FIVE: Entreat God to help you to carry out your course.

Catholic devotional practices

Pray and make the sign of the cross when passing a Catholic church: Remember that Christ is present in the church. You can offer a traditional prayer like the "Glory Be" or pray in your own words.

Pray when an emergency vehicle passes by or upon hearing a tragic news story: It's good to remember those in need. You can offer a traditional prayer or pray from your heart.

Participating in Mass

- ❖ As Catholics we are obligated to go to Mass weekly and on holy days of obligation.*
- ❖ Holy days of obligation in the United States are:
    — January 1, the Solemnity of Mary, Mother of God;
    — Thursday of the Sixth Week of Easter, the Solemnity of the Ascension;
    — August 15, the Solemnity of the Assumption of the Blessed Virgin Mary;
    — November 1, the Solemnity of All Saints;
    — December 8, the Solemnity of Mary's Immaculate Conception;
    — December 25, the Solemnity of the Nativity of Our Lord Jesus Christ.
- ❖ We are obligated to receive the Eucharist at least once during the Easter season.
- ❖ Attending daily Mass is also beneficial to our spiritual growth.

---

* Note: Christmas is always a holy day of obligation on whatever day it falls. When the feasts of the Assumption, All Saints, or the Solemnity of Mary, Mother of God (Jan. 1) are celebrated on a Saturday or Monday, there is no obligation to participate in Mass. The Immaculate Conception remains a holy day of obligation except when December 8 falls on Sunday. Then, the feast is transferred to Monday in which case it is not considered a holy day. However, the faithful are still encouraged to participate at Mass on these days. In many dioceses, the feast of the Ascension is transferred to the next Sunday.

GOING TO CONFESSION

❖ As Catholics we are obligated to confess grave sin at least once a year.

❖ Frequent Confession is also beneficial to our spiritual growth.

❖ More information can be found in the Confession guide.

Confession Guide

What Is Sin?

"Sin is an offense against God," against reason (good judgment), and against our own good. It turns our hearts away from the Lord and his love for us.[1] Sin is appealing; if it were not, no one would ever commit sin. At the heart of sin is a lie that offers false promises of happiness, peace, love, and joy. Sin never brings the sustainable peace, joy, and love that every human person longs to have. It ultimately causes harm to the sinner (sadness, depression, alienation from God, others, and self, etc.) because it turns us away from the greatest source of love, happiness, and peace—God himself.

Am I Really a Sinner?

St. John writes: "If we say we have no sin, we deceive ourselves, and the truth is not in us" (1 John 1:8).

What Is Mortal Sin?

Mortal sin is a grave act against God and his commandments in which one's friendship with God is destroyed. When one commits a mortal sin, one has knowingly, deliberately, and freely turned away from God, preferring the sin over the love of God and the truth he has revealed to us in Christ and through his Church.[2]

There are three conditions for a sin to be mortal: 1) the matter of the sin must be very serious, 2) the individual must have full knowledge of its serious nature, and 3) the individual freely chooses it.

What Is Venial Sin?

Venial sin is a minor offense against God that does not destroy but wounds our relationship with the Lord. It weakens our ability to avoid future sin.

---

1. CCC nos. 1849, 1850.
2. CCC nos. 1855–1861.

What Is the Sacrament of Reconciliation (Confession)?

The sacrament of Reconciliation is the way in which God extends his forgiveness to us. In this powerful encounter with the Lord, he grants us mercy and pardon for our sins. We are reconciled with God and others, and we receive grace to avoid sin in the future.

Why Do I Need to Go to Confession?

When you were baptized you were adopted into the family of God and received his very own divine life. This life of God within you makes you one with him and empowers you to live as Christians in the world around you.

We need to go to confession because sin can weaken or even destroy our unity with God and the very power of God within us, the graces we need to live the Christian life. Sin can jeopardize our eternal salvation.

As Catholics, we are obligated to confess mortal sins and are encouraged to confess venial sins.

Why Confess Sins to a Priest?

The Lord Jesus entrusted to the apostles his ministry of forgiveness: "Receive the Holy Spirit. If you forgive the sins of any, they are forgiven; if you retain the sins of any, they are retained" (Jn 20:22b–23). All bishops are successors of the apostles and priests are co-workers with the bishops. They continue this ministry in the world today and share in Christ's authority over sin. Jesus Christ, in his great love for us, willed that the Church should carry on his work of healing, forgiveness, and salvation through the sacrament of Reconciliation.[3]

Both the bishop and the priest stand in *"persona Christi Capitis"* (in the person of Christ the head of the Church) when administering this sacrament. This is most beautifully portrayed when, at the conclusion of the sacrament, the bishop or priest prays in the person of Christ: "I absolve you from your sins. . . ."

An Invitation . . .

"To those who have been far away from the sacrament of Reconciliation and God's forgiving love, I make this appeal: Come back to this source of grace; do not be afraid! Christ himself is waiting for you. He will heal you, and you will be at peace with God."[4]

---

3. CCC nos. 1441–1445.

4. Pope John Paul II, Apostolic Journey to the United States of America and Canada: Mass for the Faithful of San Antonio, homily," 1987, no. 6.

Making a Good Confession in Five Easy Steps

1. Pray to the Holy Spirit for the courage and grace to make an honest examination of conscience and a sincere confession.

2. Read through the Examination of Conscience (see pp. 102–105).

3. Be sorry for your sins (contrition).

4. Go to Confession.

5. Fulfill the penance the priest gives you.

1. Prayer to the Holy Spirit

Dear Holy Spirit, come into my heart and prepare my soul for this moment of grace. Grant me the gift of self-knowledge, that I may better understand the sins which keep me from you, and courage, that I may confidently confess them to your representative. Mother Mary, please stand beside me and pray for me, that I may receive this gift of mercy from your Son.

2. Examination of Conscience

First Commandment

"I am the LORD your God . . . . You shall not have other gods beside me"
(Exodus 20:2, 3).

❖ Have I doubted or denied the existence of God?

❖ Have I failed to love God and put him first in my life?

❖ Have I failed to express my love for God by making time to pray every day?

❖ Have I failed to trust in God's plan for my life?

❖ Have I received Holy Communion while in the state of mortal sin?

❖ Have I engaged or believed in superstition, fortune telling, horoscopes, good-luck charms, tarot cards, palmistry, Ouija boards, séances, reincarnation, etc.?

❖ Have I made a god out of money, drugs, alcohol, my job, TV, fame, pleasure, property, self-image, etc?

❖ Have I ever joined an organization that is opposed to the Catholic faith (for example new age cults)?

❖ Have I ever denied being a Catholic or denied a truth of the Church?

❖ Have I ever left the Catholic Church?

❖ Confess any sin(s) identified and the reason for the sin(s).

Second Commandment

"You shall not invoke the name of the Lord, your God, in vain" (Exodus 20:7).

❖ Have I used God's name in vain or irreverently in any way?

❖ Have I used the name of Jesus in this way?

❖ Have I failed to fulfill the promises I have made to God?

❖ Have I blasphemed God?

❖ Have I disrespected the Blessed Mother, the Church, or the saints through my speech (mocking, joking, irreverence, etc.)?

❖ Have I lied under oath?

❖ Have I broken an oath or a vow made in the presence of the Lord?

❖ Confess any sin(s) identified and the reason for the sin(s).

Third Commandment

"Remember the sabbath day—keep it holy" (Exodus 20:8).

❖ Have I deliberately and freely missed Mass on Sunday or holy days of obligation?

❖ Have I deliberately come to Mass late or left early?

❖ Have I unnecessarily worked on Sunday, not keeping it as a day of rest, prayer, time for family, and recreation?

❖ Confess any sin(s) identified and the reason for the sin(s).

Fourth Commandment

"Honor your father and your mother" (Exodus 20:12).

❖ Have I dishonored or disrespected my parents?

❖ Have I failed to be attentive to the needs and well-being of my family?

❖ Have I been the source of anxiety or conflict in my family?

❖ Have I failed to support and care for my parents and relatives when they were sick or elderly?

❖ Have my actions caused scandal (especially to young people), or failed to offer a good example of faith in the Lord and his Church?

❖ Have I dishonored and/or disrespected my lawful superiors?

❖ Have I failed to take the time to educate myself on the Church's teachings (especially the teachings I may struggle with)?

❖ Confess any sin(s) identified and the reason for the sin(s).

Fifth Commandment

"You shall not kill" (Exodus 20:13).

❖ Have I killed or deliberately harmed anyone?

❖ Have I had an abortion or encouraged someone to do so?

❖ Have I attempted suicide or seriously thought about it?

❖ Have I participated in or encouraged euthanasia?

❖ Have I abused alcohol or drugs?

❖ Have I been reckless in driving?

❖ Have I been gluttonous by eating much more than my fill?

❖ Do I hold anger or unforgiveness in my heart toward another?

❖ Have I acted out of anger or vengeance?

❖ Have I mutilated myself? Another?

❖ Have I taken part in direct sterilization (vasectomy, tubal ligation, etc.)?

❖ Confess any sin(s) identified and the reason for the sin(s).

Sixth and Ninth Commandments

"You shall not commit adultery" (Exodus 20:14) and
"You shall not covet your neighbor's wife" (Exodus 20:17).

❖ Have I willfully entertained impure thoughts or desires?

❖ Have I aroused my desires by impure stares or inappropriate conversations?

❖ Have I sought to read or watch something for the purpose of being aroused?

❖ Do I have friendships or acquaintances that have become inappropriate and could become a near occasion for sexual sin?

❖ Have I been impure with the use of my speech (jokes, stories, language, etc.)?

❖ Have I willfully viewed pornographic materials or media (magazines, movies, Internet, etc.), or deliberately read impure materials?

❖ Have I committed impure acts by myself (masturbation)?

❖ Have I committed impure acts with another (sexual relations outside of marriage)?

❖ Have I lived in a sexual relationship with someone outside of marriage?

❖ Have I used artificial contraception?

❖ Have I dressed immodestly?

❖ Was I married outside of the Catholic Church without the appropriate permission or dispensation?

❖ Confess any sin(s) identified and the reason for the sin(s).

Seventh and Tenth Commandments

"You shall not steal" (Exodus 20:15) and
"You shall not covet your neighbor's house" (Exodus 20:17).

❖ Have I stolen, accepted stolen property, or encouraged another to steal?

❖ Have I cheated?

❖ Have I willfully damaged or destroyed another's property?

❖ Have I gambled excessively?

❖ Have I conducted my business with dishonor or disrespect (i.e., failed to fulfill contracts, pay bills, etc.)?

❖ Have I wasted time at work?

❖ Have I treated my employees fairly and justly?

❖ Have I neglected to care for the poor and the Church according to my means?

❖ Have I been envious of what other people have (family, beauty, possessions, talents, career, etc.)?

❖ Confess any sin(s) identified and the reason for the sin(s).

Eighth Commandment

"You shall not bear false witness against your neighbor" (Exodus 20:16).

❖ Have I lied or sworn falsely?

❖ Have I revealed private information about another without good reason?

❖ Have I slandered another's reputation through useless gossip?

❖ Have I exposed the mistakes or sins of another without necessity?

❖ Have I told disparaging lies about another person?

❖ Have I plagiarized?

❖ Have I lied, or intentionally omitted confessing mortal sins, in the sacrament of Reconciliation?

❖ Confess any sin(s) identified and the reason for the sin(s).

3. Contrition

One of the essential acts of the sacrament of Reconciliation is contrition, or repentance. In this essential act the penitent, moved by God's grace, renounces the sin committed and makes a firm resolution to amend his or her life.

4. Confession

If you get nervous, ask the priest to help you. He is there as the Lord's representative to help you receive the Lord's love and mercy.

Begin by making the sign of the cross and say: "Bless me, father, for I have sinned. It has been _____ (weeks/months/years) since my last confession and these are my sins."

Confess your sins. Begin with the more difficult, more serious sins. For mortal sins, it's important to name them and the number of times they were committed.

End your confession of sins with the words: "for these and for all of my sins I am truly sorry."

The priest will offer some counsel and then assign you a penance.

PRAY AN ACT OF CONTRITION

O my God, I am heartily sorry for having offended you, and I detest all my sins because I dread the loss of heaven and the pains of hell, but most of all because they offend you, my God, who are all good and deserving of all my love. I firmly resolve, with the help of your grace, to confess my sins, to do penance and to amend my life. Amen.

The priest will then say the prayer of absolution, where the Lord frees you from sin.

5. Fulfilling Your Penance

Thank the Lord for his great mercy and then promptly fulfill the penance that was given you by the priest.

HOW TO PRAY THE ROSARY

1. Make the Sign of the Cross with the crucifix and pray the Apostles' Creed.

2. Pray one Our Father on the first bead.

3. Pray three Hail Marys on the next three beads.

4. Pray the Glory be to the Father on the small chain.

5. Announce the first mystery and pray the Our Father on the next bead.

6. Pray ten Hail Marys on the first decade of beads, and meditate on the mystery.

7. Pray the Glory be to the Father.

8. After each decade it is customary to pray the Fatima prayer: "O my Jesus, forgive us our sins, save us from the fires of hell, lead all souls to heaven, especially those who have most need of your mercy."

9. Pray the next mystery following the same procedure, and repeat until the five decades are complete.

10. Then pray the Hail, Holy Queen.

Sign of the Cross

In the name of the Father, and of the Son, and of the Holy Spirit. Amen.

The Apostles' Creed

I believe in God,
the Father almighty,
Creator of heaven and earth,
and in Jesus Christ, his only Son, our Lord,
who was conceived by the Holy Spirit,
born of the Virgin Mary,
suffered under Pontius Pilate,
was crucified, died and was buried;

he descended into hell;

on the third day he rose again from the dead;

he ascended into heaven,

and is seated at the right hand of God the Father almighty;

from there he will come to judge the living and the dead.

I believe in the Holy Spirit,

the holy catholic Church,

the communion of saints,

the forgiveness of sins,

the resurrection of the body,

and life everlasting. Amen.

Our Father

Our Father who art in heaven, hallowed be thy name; thy kingdom come, thy will be done on earth as it is in heaven. Give us this day our daily bread, and forgive us our trespasses, as we forgive those who trespass against us. And lead us not into temptation, but deliver us from evil. Amen.

Hail Mary

Hail Mary, full of grace, the Lord is with you. Blessed are you among women and blessed is the fruit of your womb, Jesus. Holy Mary, Mother of God, pray for us sinners, now and at the hour of our death. Amen.

Glory Be

Glory be to the Father, and to the Son, and to the Holy Spirit. As it was in the beginning, is now, and ever shall be, world without end. Amen.

Hail, Holy Queen

Hail, Holy Queen, Mother of Mercy, our life, our sweetness and our hope! To you do we cry, poor banished children of Eve; to you do we send up our sighs, mourning, and weeping in this valley of tears. Turn then, most gracious advocate, your eyes of mercy toward us, and after this our exile, show unto us the blessed fruit of your womb, Jesus. O clement, O loving, O sweet Virgin Mary!

V. Pray for us, O Holy Mother of God.

R. That we may be made worthy of the promises of Christ.

Let us pray. O God, whose only begotten Son, by his life, death, and resurrection, has purchased for us the rewards of eternal life, grant, we beseech you, that by meditating upon these mysteries of the Most Holy Rosary of the Blessed Virgin Mary, we may imitate what they contain and obtain what they promise, through the same Christ Our Lord. Amen.

The Rosary is a prayer that involves praying and reflecting on events in the life of Jesus and Mary. We call these events "mysteries." With each mystery, we reflect on the virtues practiced by Jesus and Mary.

❖ The Rosary is a Christ-centered prayer, even though it involves repeating many Hail Marys. It is to contemplate with Mary the life, death, and resurrection of Jesus.

❖ The Rosary can be prayed alone or with others. It can be prayed in its entirety or one decade at a time.

Tips for praying the rosary:

❖ Use opportune times to pray the Rosary, i.e., car rides, walks in the park, or while waiting for someone or for an appointment.

❖ Make it a part of your daily routine, i.e., every night before bed.

❖ Be familiar with the Scripture stories and events recalled in each mystery.

❖ Make the Rosary your "emergency prayer," to be prayed when all other words and thoughts fail you.

❖ Pray each decade for a particular intention.

❖ Pray for the particular virtue associated with each mystery.

❖ Reflect: How well am I living this virtue? How might I live this virtue today?

Mystery	Grace to Ask
THE FIVE JOYFUL MYSTERIES Prayed on Monday and Saturday	
The Annunciation	Humility
The Visitation	Charity or love of neighbor
The Birth of Our Lord	Simplicity or detachment from worldly goods
The Presentation of Our Lord	Obedience to God
The Finding of Our Lord in the Temple	Perseverance in seeking the Lord

Mystery	Grace to Ask
THE FIVE LUMINOUS MYSTERIES Prayed on Thursday	
The Baptism of Jesus in the Jordan	Faithfulness to Baptismal promises
The Wedding at Cana	Trust in Mary's intercession
The Proclamation of the Kingdom	Willingness to serve the Lord
The Transfiguration	Holiness
The Institution of the Eucharist	Reverence and love for Christ in the Eucharist

Mystery	Grace to Ask
THE FIVE SORROWFUL MYSTERIES Prayed on Tuesday and Friday	
The Agony in the Garden	Sorrow for our sins
The Scourging	Control over our senses or purity
The Crowning with Thorns	Moral courage
The Carrying of the Cross	Patient endurance/perseverance
The Crucifixion and Death of Our Lord	Self-sacrifice/sacrificial love

Mystery	Grace to Ask
THE FIVE GLORIOUS MYSTERIES Prayed on Wednesday and Sunday	
The Resurrection	Faith
The Ascension	Desire for heaven
The Descent of the Holy Spirit	Openness to the Holy Spirit
The Assumption of Our Blessed Mother into Heaven	Hope
The Coronation of Our Blessed Mother	Devotion to Mary

SPIRITUAL PRACTICES
FOR MARRIAGE AND FAMILY LIFE ACTIVITY

Directions: Go through the list of items and

 Place a ✔ in the first column for spiritual practices you *currently do.*

 Place a ✔ in the second column for spiritual practices you want to *start to do.*

 Place a ✔ in the third column for spiritual practices you want to do as a *couple.*

 Place a ✔ in the fourth column for spiritual practices you want to do as a *family.*

Spiritual Practice*	Currently do	Want to start	Want to do as a couple	Want to do as a family
Attend Sunday Mass.				
Attend daily Mass.				
Go to Confession.				
Pray at the beginning of the day.				
Pray throughout the day.				
Pray at the end of the day.				
Examen prayer (examination of conscience).				
Pray before meals.				
Pray after meals.				
Quiet personal prayer.				
Pray the Rosary.				
Eucharistic Adoration.				
Visit the Lord present in the tabernacle.				
Pray when passing a Catholic church.				
Pray when an emergency vehicle passes by.				
Read the Bible.				

*For examples and ideas for how to do each of these, please see the resources on pp. 95ff.

Spiritual Practice	Currently do	Want to start	Want to do as a couple	Want to do as a family
Know how to hear God's voice and direction.				
Know people who are "spiritual mentors."				
Have a "spiritual director."				
Pay attention to the "coincidences in life" to listen to how God is speaking.				
Periodically, reflect on our interactions with others, the events in our life and in our marriage to hear God speaking.				
Participate in spiritual enrichment programs.				
Read books that will nurture faith.				
Access good information from Catholic radio, TV, and websites.				
Attend faith formation/Bible study groups.				
Attend a retreat.				
Regularly practice repentance as a couple.				
Have friends who can help us grow in faith.				
Belong to a parish.				
Serve the parish in any capacity.				
Feed the hungry.				
Give drink to the thirsty.				
Clothe the naked.				
Shelter the homeless.				

Spiritual Practice	Currently do	Want to start	Want to do as a couple	Want to do as a family
Visit the sick.				
Visit the imprisoned.				
Bury the dead.				
Counsel the doubtful.				
Instruct the ignorant.				
Admonish sinners.				
Comfort the afflicted.				
Forgive offenses.				
Bear wrongs patiently.				
Pray for the living and the dead.				

TAKE HOME ACTIVITY

Discussion questions for couples preparing for an ccumenical marriage

Please take time to honestly and openly discuss the following questions with one another. Your respective clergy can offer support and guidance.

1. What are some religious beliefs and values we share?

2. Where will we worship each week and on religious holidays?

3. Are there any religious beliefs we feel may be a source of conflict? If so, which beliefs, and how might we address any conflict?

4. What areas of parenting could be affected by our different religious beliefs and practices?

5. How can we support one another in our respective faith traditions?

6. How will we celebrate religious holidays and holy days?

7. Do our families have any reservations or concerns in this regard?

8. How will we honor the Catholic Church's expectation that our children will be raised in the Catholic faith?

9. What challenges do we foresee?

10. How can our faith be a source of growth and unity in our marriage?

The Teaching Mass

The Presence of Christ:
The Cornerstone of Our Marriage

"Whoever eats my flesh
and drinks my blood
remains in me and I in him."
John 6:56

HOUSE METAPHOR

- ❧ The cornerstone is the first stone set in the foundation, thus determining the position of the entire structure.

- ❧ As Christians, Jesus is our cornerstone, the most important part of your foundation, upon which the rest of your marriage is built.

GOAL OF THIS TOPIC

- ❧ *Be wise* and *be faithful*: For Catholics, the Teaching Mass is an opportunity to deepen your Catholic faith, your devotion to the Eucharist, and your understanding of the importance of the Mass. For non-Catholics, the Teaching Mass is an introduction and exposure to the celebration that is central to the faith of your future spouse.

Why is the Mass a part of this program?

- ❖ The Mass is the most important, central, and sacred act of worship in Catholicism.

- ❖ The Mass and the Eucharist will continue to be a central source of grace for married couples to love each other and their family more fully.

- ❖ As Catholic disciples of Christ, it is our obligation, but also our privilege, to attend Mass on the Lord's Day and feast days and more often, if possible.

- ❖ When we go to Mass, we go out of love to be further transformed in love, through the Holy Spirit.

The Mass is

1. The Mass is thanksgiving and praise to the Father.[1]

    - ❖ We thank God and praise God for the life, death, and resurrection of his Son.

2. The Mass is the sacrificial memorial of Christ and his Body.[2]

    - ❖ The Mass makes present the sacrifice of Christ on the cross.

    - ❖ At the Last Supper, Jesus asked us to do this in memory of him.

---

1. CCC no. 1358.
2. Ibid.

3. The Mass is the presence of Christ.[3] We encounter the presence of Christ in four ways:

   a. Christ is present in the *Christian community* celebrating: God is in each of us and is present when two or more are gathered together.

   b. Christ is present in the *Word* proclaimed: Scripture is the Word of God.

   c. Christ is present in the *priest presiding:* the ordained priest acts in the person of Christ.

   d. Christ is present, most importantly, in the *Eucharist.*

      ❖ During Mass, the priest consecrates the bread and wine, just as Jesus did at the Last Supper. The bread and wine become the Body and Blood of Jesus even though they still look, feel, and taste like bread and wine.

      ❖ The Eucharist nourishes our soul.

      ❖ Jesus remains with us in the Eucharist even after Mass.

4. The Mass is a means of grace.

   ❖ The Mass is the most effective source of grace we have on earth, and our dispositions affect the grace we receive.[4]

   ❖ Graces communicated by the sacrifice of the Mass include:

      — Increased union with Jesus.

      — Forgiveness of less serious (venial) sin.

      — Protection from serious (mortal) sin.

      — Strength for the challenges and temptations of daily life.

      — Union with fellow Catholics and the Church in heaven.[5]

      — Gives us a pledge of eternal life.

---

3. CCC no. 1373, and *Sacrosanctum Concilium* no. 7.

4. See John A. Hardon, S.J., *The Sacrifice Sacrament of the Holy Eucharist*, 1998, accessed on May 2012 at http://www.therealpresence.org/archives/Mass/Mass_008.htm.

5. See CCC nos. 1416–1419.

Tour of the church (and sacred vessels)

The church and its sacred objects all serve to enhance the celebration of Mass and bring us closer to God.

ALTAR: Where the unbloody re-presentation of the sacrifice of Christ on the cross takes place. It is not a new sacrifice, but it makes the original, complete sacrifice of Jesus present again.

BREAD: Unleavened bread, made only of wheat and flour, that is consecrated into the Body of Christ.

WINE: Fermented grape juice that is consecrated into the Blood of Christ.

PATEN: A plate-like disk that holds the bread that becomes the Body of Christ.

CHALICE: The large cup used to hold the wine that becomes the Blood of Christ.

CIBORIUM: A vessel used to hold the hosts that will be used for Communion.

CORPORAL: A square linen cloth placed on the altar during the offertory to catch any particles of consecrated bread or wine that may spill.

CRUETS: Small pitchers used to hold water and the wine that will be consecrated.

PALL: The stiff, square, white cover to protect the contents of the chalice.

PYX: A small, pocket-size receptacle used by priests and Eucharistic ministers to carry consecrated hosts to the sick and those unable to attend Mass.

TABERNACLE: Where the Body of Christ is reserved in the church.

SANCTUARY LAMP: A candle that continuously burns near the tabernacle to remind us of Christ's presence.

MONSTRANCE: A sacred vessel that holds the consecrated host for Eucharistic Adoration.

LECTERN/AMBO/PULPIT: A pulpit from which the Word of God is proclaimed.

BAPTISMAL FONT: A large basin, often made of stone, where Baptisms take place.

HOLY WATER FONT: A small basin that contains blessed water and is usually found near the entrance of a church. When we enter the Church, we bless ourselves with the water as a reminder of our Baptism, and to ask for forgiveness of less serious (venial) sins.

HOLY OILS: Holy oils are blessed by the bishop and used in certain sacraments, such as Baptism and Anointing of the Sick.

Structure of a Church:

NARTHEX: Entryway or vestibule of a church.

NAVE: Main part of the church.

SANCTUARY: Where the altar and tabernacle stand.

SACRISTY: An area near the sanctuary where the sacred vessels and vestments are kept and prepared for Mass. It is usually located near the sanctuary.

The Priest's Vestments

The priest's vestments are rich in symbolism and serve a purpose:

ALB: The long plain white garment that symbolizes our Baptism and purity.

STOLE: A scarf-like cloth that represents holy orders and is worn anytime a sacrament is administered.

CHASUBLE: This is the outer vestment, usually in the liturgical color of the season.

Liturgical Colors

Liturgical colors symbolize the deeper realities we celebrate and help us to worship in the spirit of the season.

WHITE: The color of joy, victory, and purity, is used during the Christmas and Easter seasons, and on feasts of Christ, Mary, and some saints. As a reminder of the resurrection it is also used at funerals (purple or black may also be used.) Gold may also be used on solemn occasions.

RED: The color of fire and blood is used on the days when we celebrate the passion of Jesus—Passion (Palm) Sunday and Good Friday.

GREEN: The color of life, is used during Ordinary Time. Ordinary does not mean routine or basic, but refers to the weeks of the liturgical year outside the special seasons (Advent, Christmas, Lent, and Easter).

PURPLE: The color of penance, repentance, and renewal is used during Advent and Lent as we prepare for the birth and resurrection of Christ.

ROSE: The color of joy, is an optional color used on the Third Sunday of Advent (Gaudete Sunday), and on the Fourth Sunday of Lent (Laetare Sunday). It expresses joyful anticipation for Christmas and Easter.

Suggestion: Decorate a prayer space in your home with liturgical colors to infuse your daily life with the seasons of the Church year. Practice the traditional disciplines of Lent and Advent, i.e., prayer, fasting, and sacrificial giving. Participate in additional devotions during the seasons of Advent and Lent, i.e., the Stations of the Cross.

Structure of the Mass

INTRODUCTORY RITES: This is the gathering part of the celebration when we prepare our hearts, minds, and souls to hear the Word of God and then receive Christ in the Eucharist.

LITURGY OF THE WORD: This is the story telling part of the celebration when we hear from Sacred Scripture about how God has interacted with us throughout history, and we reflect on the message of God for our lives today.

LITURGY OF THE EUCHARIST: This is the meal sharing part of our celebration when the bread and wine become the Body and Blood of Jesus. It is also the sacrificial memorial of Christ's Paschal Mystery. Those in communion with the Catholic Church are invited to receive Jesus in Holy Communion.

CONCLUDING RITES: This is the commissioning part of our celebration encouraging us to take what we have received and share it with others.

INSPIRING WORDS

To Catholics who have been away from Sunday Mass.[6]

My dear brothers and sisters: please know that we miss you, we love you, and we hope you will rejoin our Catholic family for our Sunday Mass.

Some of you have drifted away from the Church and have been waiting for a good time to return. I pray that you will consider this the time to join us on our faith journey toward Heaven. The sacred teachings of the Church offer guidance, direction, and meaning in a world where so many cannot find their way. Our faith points us to Jesus, who is 'the Way, the Truth and the Life' (John 14:6).

Some of you have made a choice to stop coming to Church because you have been hurt by the actions of someone in the Church or because of a difficulty with a Church teaching. From my first day as Archbishop of Boston and perhaps for the rest of my days, I will always be asking the forgiveness of all those who have been hurt by the actions, or inaction, of people and leaders in the Church. Please do not let those experiences and memories separate you from the love of Christ and of our Catholic family and prevent you from receiving the grace of the sacraments.

When we launched the Catholics Come Home initiative on Ash Wednesday, a reporter asked me what I would say to Catholics who do not attend Mass because they disagree with or have questions about Church teaching. I answered that our teaching does not change because people disagree with it; our faith comes from Christ's own teaching in the Scriptures and through the teaching authority of the Church throughout the ages. We recognize, however, that many struggle to reconcile Church teaching with social norms in American society today; to them, we say that we want to engage in a meaningful conversation with you. We want you to know that you are part of our family. We want to assure you that God loves you and waits for you at Sunday Mass. The best place to begin a conversation is by gathering with the family of believers in the worshiping community.

To those who consider themselves unwelcome at Mass because of some irregularity or moral struggle, please know that you are always loved by God, and the Catholic community desires your presence with us. We are all brothers and sisters in Christ. An inability to fulfill all aspects of Christian worship or to receive Communion should not keep you

---

6. Cardinal Seán P. O'Malley, OFM Cap., *Jesus's Eager Desire: Our Participation in the Sunday Mass,* November 20, 2011.

from Mass. In fact, the habit of being faithful to the Sunday obligation can provide the actual grace, if you cooperate with it, to give you the strength to overcome current obstacles and find paths of reconciliation. We stand ready to help you.

On the True Presence of Christ in the Eucharist[7]

The Eucharist is *not just something symbolic.* Jesus said: "I am the living bread that came down from heaven; if any one eats of this bread, he will live forever; . . . he who eats my flesh and drinks my blood has eternal life and . . . abides in me, and I in him." *Upon hearing these words many disciples abandoned Jesus but he did not call them back and say, "I am just kidding," or "these are just figurative expressions."* Instead he asks the apostles if they are going to leave him too. Saint Peter answers in the name of all faithful disciples: "Lord, to whom shall we go? You have the words of eternal life."

7. Ibid.

WORSHIP AID FOR THE TEACHING MASS

Active Participation: Before even going to Mass, we can prepare with: 1) study (for example, reading the Scriptures for the Mass, becoming aware of the liturgical season, etc.); 2) thought (for example, review our life since our last Mass: problems, decisions, concerns, or joys to intentionally bring to Mass); 3) prayer (for example, any prayer intentions we would like to bring and offer. Just as a priest offers Mass for a special intention, we can offer our prayers as well).

INTRODUCTORY RITES

Active Participation: We can arrive for Mass a few minutes early to quiet our busy minds, offer our special intentions for the Mass, and ask the Holy Spirit to help us participate prayerfully and receive Jesus worthily.

   All rise for Mass as the priest enters.

Entrance Song or Chant

Greeting

Priest: The Lord be with you.
People: **And with your spirit.**

Active Participation: We should repent of any actions or attitudes that have separated us from God and others and ask for his forgiveness.

Penitential Act

Form A

**I confess to almighty God
and to you, my brothers and sisters,
that I have greatly sinned,
in my thoughts and in my words,
in what I have done and in what
      I have failed to do,
through my fault, through my fault,
through my most grievous fault,
therefore I ask blessed Mary ever-Virgin,
all the Angels and Saints,
and you, my brothers and sisters,
to pray for me to the Lord our God.**

> Strike chest three times, at each time you say "fault."

FORM B

Priest: Have mercy on us, O Lord.

People: **For we have sinned against you.**

Priest: Show us, O Lord, your mercy.

People: **And grant us your salvation.**

GLORIA

Glory to God in the highest,

and on earth peace to people of good will.

We praise you,

we bless you,

we adore you,

we glorify you,

we give you thanks for your great glory,

Lord God, heavenly King,

O God, almighty Father.

Lord Jesus Christ, Only Begotten Son,

Lord God, Lamb of God, Son of the Father,

you take away the sins of the world,

have mercy on us;

you take away the sins of the world,

receive our prayer;

you are seated at the right hand of the Father,

have mercy on us.

For you alone are the Holy One,

you alone are the Lord,

you alone are the Most High,

Jesus Christ,

with the Holy Spirit,

in the glory of God the Father.

Amen.

COLLECT (OPENING PRAYER)

LITURGY OF THE WORD

All are seated for the readings.

Active Participation: Scripture is relevant to us. We should expect that God will have a message for us in the readings or homily and we should listen intently for how God is speaking to us through a word, phrase, answer to prayer, etc. After the Mass, in our daily life, we can try to recall what we heard. This allows the Word of God to transform us.

FIRST READING

RESPONSORIAL PSALM

SECOND READING

All rise for the Gospel reading.

GOSPEL ACCLAMATION (ALLELUIA AND CHANT)

GOSPEL READING

Deacon (or Priest): A reading from the holy Gospel according to N.
People: **Glory to you, O Lord.**

After the Gospel is read, the people respond: **Praise to you Lord Jesus Christ.**

Active Participation: As we say, "Praise to you Lord Jesus Christ," a good habit to develop is to quietly say to ourselves, "May your Word always be on my mind, on my lips, and in my heart" as we make the sign of the cross on our forehead, over our mouth, and over our heart.

All are seated for the homily.

HOMILY

All rise to profess our faith.

NICENE CREED

I believe in one God,
the Father almighty,
maker of heaven and earth,
of all things visible and invisible.
I believe in one Lord Jesus Christ,
the Only Begotten Son of God,
born of the Father before all ages.
God from God, Light from Light,
true God from true God,
begotten, not made, consubstantial with the Father;
through him all things were made.
For us men and for our salvation
he came down from heaven,
**and by the Holy Spirit was incarnate of
the Virgin Mary,**
and became man.
For our sake he was crucified under Pontius Pilate,

At the words that follow,
up to and including
"and became man,"
all bow.

he suffered death and was buried,
and rose again on the third day
in accordance with the Scriptures.
He ascended into heaven
and is seated at the right hand of the Father.
He will come again in glory
to judge the living and the dead
and his kingdom will have no end.
I believe in the Holy Spirit, the Lord, the giver of life,
who proceeds from the Father and the Son,
who with the Father and the Son is adored and glorified,
who has spoken through the prophets.
I believe in one, holy, catholic and apostolic Church.
I confess one Baptism for the forgiveness of sins
and I look forward to the resurrection of the dead
and the life of the world to come. Amen.

Universal Prayer (Prayer of the Faithful)

All are seated as the altar is prepared for the Liturgy of the Eucharist.
If an offering is collected, it is collected at this time.

LITURGY OF THE EUCHARIST

Presentation and Preparation of the Gifts (Offertory)

Active Participation: At the offertory, we can offer what we have—the gift of our life to God. We pray that God will transform us into the Body of Christ, which we receive.

Priest: Blessed are you, Lord God of all creation,
for through your goodness we have received
the bread we offer you:
fruit of the earth and work of human hands,
it will become for us the bread of life.

People: **Blessed be God for ever.**

Priest: Blessed are you, Lord God of all creation,
for through your goodness we have received
the wine we offer you:
fruit of the vine and work of human hands,
it will become our spiritual drink.

People: **Blessed be God for ever.**

INVITATION TO PRAYER

Priest: Pray, brethren (brothers and sisters),
        that my sacrifice and yours
        may be acceptable to God,
        the almighty Father.

All stand.

People: **May the Lord accept the sacrifice at your hands**
        for the praise and glory of his name,
        for our good
        and the good of all his holy Church.

THE EUCHARISTIC PRAYER

PREFACE DIALOGUE

Priest: The Lord be with you.
People: **And with your spirit.**
Priest: Lift up your hearts.
People: **We lift them up to the Lord.**
Priest: Let us give thanks to the Lord our God.
People: **It is right and just.**

SANCTUS

Holy, Holy, Holy Lord God of hosts.
Heaven and earth are full of your glory.
Hosanna in the highest.
Blessed is he who comes in the name of the Lord.
Hosanna in the highest.

The priest will pray the Eucharistic Prayer.

All kneel for the consecration of the bread and wine.

THE MYSTERY OF FAITH

Priest: The mystery of faith.
People: **We proclaim your Death, O Lord,**
        and profess your Resurrection
        until you come again.

OR:

When we eat this Bread and drink
  this Cup,
we proclaim your Death, O Lord,
until you come again.

OR:

Save us, Savior of the world,
for by your Cross and Resurrection
you have set us free.

Concluding Doxology

People: **Amen.**

All stand for the beginning of the Communion Rite.

Active Participation: We can pray each line of the Our Father with sincerity and intention.

The Lord's Prayer

People: **Our Father, who art in heaven,**
   hallowed be thy name;
   thy kingdom come,
   thy will be done
   on earth as it is in heaven.
   Give us this day our daily bread,
   and forgive us our trespasses,
   as we forgive those who trespass against us.
   And lead us not into temptation,
   but deliver us from evil.

The priest continues praying.

People: **For the kingdom,**
   the power and the glory are yours
   now and forever.

Sign of Peace

Priest: The peace of the Lord be with you always.
People: **And with your spirit.**

Lamb of God

Lamb of God, you take away the sins of the world,
 have mercy on us.
Lamb of God, you take away the sins of the world,
 have mercy on us.
Lamb of God, you take away the sins of the world,
 grant us peace.

All kneel until the distribution of Holy Communion and remain kneeling after returning to their seats until the sacred vessels have been purified.

Invitation to Communion

Priest: Behold the Lamb of God,
   behold him who takes away the sins of the world.
   Blessed are those called to the supper of the Lamb.

All: **Lord, I am not worthy**
      that you should enter under my roof,
      but only say the word
      and my soul shall be healed.

COMMUNION

Active Participation: In Holy Communion we meet and receive Christ. In this time of silence, we can offer Jesus our gratitude for all the blessings in our life, especially our relationship with him, or sit silently to listen to what God has to say to us.

Guidelines for the Reception of Communion[8]

For Catholics: As Catholics, we fully participate in the celebration of the Eucharist when we receive Holy Communion. We are encouraged to receive Communion devoutly and frequently. In order to be properly disposed to receive Communion, participants should not be conscious of grave sin and normally should have fasted for one hour. A person who is conscious of grave sin is not to receive the Body and Blood of the Lord without prior sacramental confession except for a grave reason where there is no opportunity for confession. In this case, the person is to be mindful of the obligation to make an act of perfect contrition, including the intention of confessing as soon as possible (canon 916). A frequent reception of the sacrament of Penance is encouraged for all.

For our fellow Christians: We welcome our fellow Christians to this celebration of the Eucharist as our brothers and sisters. We pray that our common baptism and the action of the Holy Spirit in this Eucharist will draw us closer to one another and begin to dispel the sad divisions which separate us. We pray that these will lessen and finally disappear, in keeping with Christ's prayer for us "that they may all be one" (John 17:21). Because Catholics believe that the celebration of the Eucharist is a sign of the reality of the oneness of faith, life, and worship, members of those churches with whom we are not yet fully united are ordinarily not admitted to Holy Communion. Eucharistic sharing in exceptional circumstances by other Christians requires permission according to the directives of the diocesan bishop and the provisions of canon law (canon 844 § 4). Members of the Orthodox Churches, the Assyrian Church of the East, and the Polish National Catholic Church are urged to respect the discipline of their own Churches. According to Roman Catholic discipline, the Code of Canon Law does not object to the reception of communion by Christians of these Churches (canon 844 §3).

For those not receiving Holy Communion: All who are not receiving Holy Communion are encouraged to express in their hearts a prayerful desire for unity with the Lord Jesus and with one another.

---

8. USCCB, accessed May 2012 at http://old.usccb.org/liturgy/current/intercom.shtml.

For non-Christians: We also welcome to this celebration those who do not share our faith in Jesus Christ. While we cannot admit them to Holy Communion, we ask them to offer their prayers for the peace and the unity of the human family.

SACRED SILENCE

PRAYER AFTER COMMUNION

THE CONCLUDING RITES

All stand.

ANNOUNCEMENTS (IF THERE ARE ANY)

FINAL BLESSING

DISMISSAL

RECESSIONAL HYMN

Active participation: After the Mass has ended, we can remain in quiet prayer with the Lord to thank him for the gift of the Eucharist and prepare to carry him with us always.

TOPIC 11

Marital Sexuality

A Divine Design:
The Architect's Plan
to Nurture Love and Life

"God created mankind in his image;
in the image of God he created them;
male and female he created them.
God blessed them and God said to them:
Be fertile and multiply; fill the earth
and subdue it."

GENESIS 1:27, 28

HOUSE METAPHOR

- Just as an architect has a purpose for his plans, so too, God has a purpose for sexual intercourse and marital sexuality.

GOALS OF THIS TOPIC

- *Be wise* and *be true*: To help you understand the nature and purposes of the marital act and the way in which it consummates and renews your vows.

- *Be wise* and *be skilled*: To help you understand the scientific basis of Natural Family Planning.

- *Be wise* and *be skilled*: To help you understand Natural Family Planning methods and their efficacy.

- *Be wise*: To help you explore perceived obstacles to Natural Family Planning use.

- *Be wise*: To help you understand the differences between contraception and Natural Family Planning.

- *Be faithful*: To help you understand the Church's teachings regarding reproductive technologies.

"Man and woman are created individually in the image and likeness of God, and are called to live in a communion of love, in this way they mirror to the world the image of God."

Blessed John Paul II
Mulieris Dignitatem, no. 7

PRE-PRESENTATION ACTIVITY

Section A

Briefly complete the following statements. We will be looking for volunteers to share their answers to the first two statements.

1. The marital act is . . . _____

    _____

2. The marital act is for . . . _____

    _____

3. I get my information on sexuality from . . . _____

    _____

4. The family planning method that we are most strongly considering is . . .

    _____

Section B

Circle your response to each of the following statements.

SA (strongly agree), A (agree), U (uncertain), D (disagree), SD (strongly disagree).

1. The information we have received regarding family planning is helping us consider a family planning method that is safe, effective, and easy to use.

    SA   A   U   D   SD

2. It is important that we both share equally in family planning.

    SA   A   U   D   SD

3. The best family planning methods would be effective for both achieving and preventing pregnancy.

    SA   A   U   D   SD

4. We have a good understanding of all forms of family planning.

    SA   A   U   D   SD

SECTION C

Please indicate **T** (true) or **F** (false) on the lines below.

1. Menstruation occurs every 28 days. _____

2. Pregnancy is possible with every act of intercourse. _____

3. A woman has biological signs that indicate the days when pregnancy can occur. _____

4. Ovulation (the release of an egg cell) occurs on day 14 in the menstrual cycle. _____

5. Once released, an egg cell can be fertilized for 48 hours. _____

6. Sperm will survive in the female reproductive system for three to five days after intercourse. _____

7. Infertility affects about 10 percent of couples in the United States. _____

8. Natural family planning methods are highly effective at avoiding pregnancy. _____

The marital act is

- ❖ Sexual intercourse between husband and wife
- ❖ A form of communication
- ❖ The consummation, expression, and renewal of vows
- ❖ An outward sign of the sacrament of Marriage
- ❖ An expression of marital love: free, total, faithful, fruitful, sacrificial

The marital act is for

- ❖ Love/Unity/Bonding
- ❖ Life/Children/Babies

Fertility awareness information can be used to*

- ❖ Achieve pregnancy
- ❖ Postpone pregnancy
- ❖ Diagnose and treat reproductive disorders including infertility

What does a woman's cycle look like?

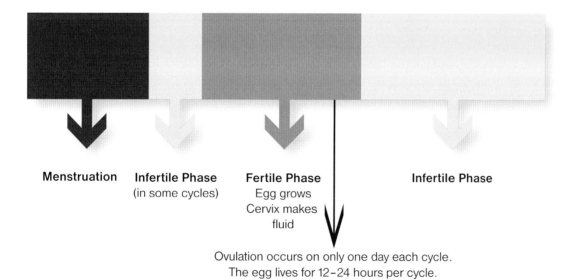

Menstruation **Infertile Phase** (in some cycles) **Fertile Phase** Egg grows Cervix makes fluid **Infertile Phase**

Ovulation occurs on only one day each cycle.
The egg lives for 12–24 hours per cycle.

---

* The following information is not to be used for self-instruction in Natural Family Planning nor as a substitute for instruction by a certified Natural Family Planning instructor.

Where is the fertile phase?

Due to cycle variations, the fertile phase moves.

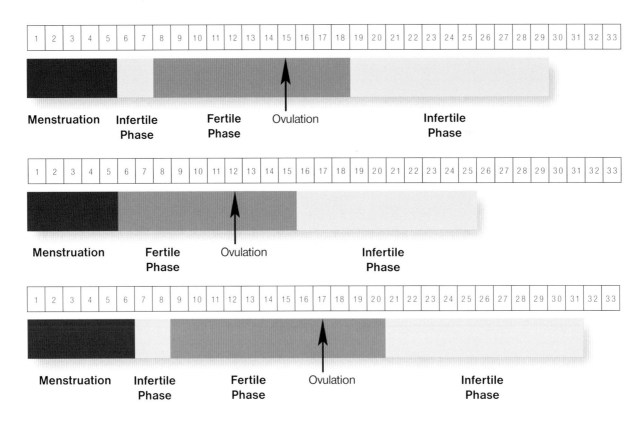

How do we identify the fertile phase?

a) Fertility signs that a woman can observe each day identify the fertile window.

❖ Changes in resting body temp (basal body temperature)

❖ Changes in cervical fluid

❖ Changes in female hormones

b) Cycle data and formulas can also help to identify the fertile phase.

Couple fertility—in order for pregnancy to occur:

❖ Sperm,

❖ Egg, and

❖ Cervical fluid need to be present.

— The egg lives 12–24 hours after ovulation.

— In the presence of cervical fluid, sperm live three to five days in the woman's reproductive system.

Responsible and generous parenthood

a) Family planning is a privilege and responsibility of the married couple to decide with love and generosity when and how many children they will have.

   ❖ Provided: The motive is just and the means are moral.

b) Couples should be both responsible and generous in welcoming children.

c) Couples may postpone a pregnancy for just reasons:

   ❖ Physical reasons

   ❖ Economic reasons

   ❖ Psychological reasons

   ❖ Social reasons

d) Responsibilities to God, marriage relationship, children and society must be taken into account in determining just reasons for postponing pregnancy. Couples are asked to maintain a proper set of priorities.

How does NFP work?

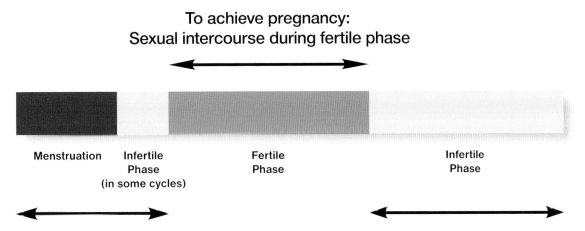

To achieve pregnancy:
Sexual intercourse during fertile phase

| Menstruation | Infertile Phase (in some cycles) | Fertile Phase | Infertile Phase |

To avoid pregnancy: Postpone sexual intercourse during fertile phase

Natural Family Planning: NFP methods

❖ Standard Days Method

❖ Ovulation Method

❖ Basal Body Temperature Method

❖ Sympto-Thermal Method

❖ Sympto-Hormonal Method (This method has several models, such as the Marquette Model or the Archdiocese of Boston Cross-Check Method.)

❖ Lactational Amenorrhea (full breastfeeding)

Method	Formula and Cycle Data	Cervical Fluid	Temperature	Monitor
Standard Days	✓			
Ovulation Method		✓		
Basal Body Temperature	✓		✓	
Sympto-Thermal	✓	✓	✓	
Sympto-Hormonal	✓	✓	✓	✓
Lactational Amenorrhea (full breastfeeding)	Used in the first six months postpartum. No monitoring done.			

Efficacy of NFP

Modern methods of NFP compete very effectively with methods of contraception, while respecting the purpose and meaning of the marital act, and without harmful side effects.

EFFICACY OF FAMILY PLANNING METHODS

Methods	Range of Effectiveness[*]
Pill[†]	99.7%–91%
NuvaRing[†]	99.7%–91%
Natural Family Planning Methods[‡]	99.6%–85%
Condoms[†]	98%–82%
Withdrawal[†]	96%–78%
No method[†]	15%

[*] Rates are calculated on 100 women over 12 months. The range of effectiveness reflects the range of method efficacy among correct and total users of a method (including incorrect users). Correct users of a method have a higher method efficacy and incorrect users have a lower method efficacy.

[†] Trussell J. "Contraceptive Efficacy" in *Contraceptive Technology Twentieth Revised Edition*, R. A. Hatcher et. al. (New York: Ardent Media, 2011), 50.

[‡] Statistics compiled from the following method-specific efficacy studies:

Arevalo, M., Jennings, et. al., "Efficacy of a New Method of Family Planning: the Standard Day Method," *Contraception*, 65 (2002): 333–338.

Arevalo M. Jennings, et. al., "Efficacy of the New TwoDay Method of Family Planning," *Fertility and Sterility*, 2004; 82;885–892.

Fehring, R. J., et. al., "Efficacy of Cervical Mucus Observations Plus Electronic Hormonal Fertility Monitoring as a Method of Natural Family Planning," *Journal of Obstetric, Gynecological, and Neonatal Nursing*, 2007;36:152–160.

Frank-Hermann, P., et. al., "The Effectiveness of a Fertility Awareness Based Method to Avoid Pregnancy in Relation to a Couple's Sexual Behavior During the Fertile Time: A Prospective Longitudinal Study," *Human Reproduction*, 2007; 22:1310–1319.

J. Trussell and L. Grummer-Strawn, "Contraceptive Failure of the Ovulation Method of Periodic Abstinence," *Family Planning Perspectives*, 22 (1990): 65–75.

What is the difference between contraception and NFP?

a) Contraception acts against fertilization and/or implantation.

b) Contraceptive use does not integrate both purposes of sexual intercourse and does not accept the fertility naturally present at any time.

c) NFP does not work against fertilization and/or implantation.

d) NFP use integrates both purposes of sexual intercourse and accepts the fertility naturally present at all times.

The action of the couple in using NFP is different from contraception

a) Natural Family Planning (to avoid pregnancy):

   ❖ Couple arranges the pattern, that is, the timing of sexual intercourse.

   ❖ No sexual intercourse during the fertile window.

   ❖ No matter when the couple has sexual intercourse, fertility is exchanged to the extent that it is naturally present.

   ❖ The couple never takes any action before, during, or after any act of sexual intercourse to render the marital act sterile, incomplete, or to prevent implantation of a fertilized egg.

b) Contraception:

   ❖ A couple alters sexual intercourse and/or the reproductive system.

   ❖ The sexual intercourse is made sterile or incomplete by the couple.

   ❖ In every act of sexual intercourse the couple takes a deliberate act before, during, or after sexual intercourse to render the marital act sterile, incomplete, or to prevent implantation of a fertilized egg.

   ❖ Intent, circumstance, and the end is the same, but this couple is doing something very different.

Infertility rule of thumb

New life is conceived:

   1. in the body
   2. through an act of intercourse
   3. by the spouses.

Resources

- ❖ Billings Ovulation Method Association—U.S.A. (BOMA): http://www.boma-usa.org/
- ❖ Couple to Couple League International (CCL): http://www.ccli.org/
- ❖ Family of the Americas Foundation (FAF): http://www.familyplanning.net
- ❖ Marquette University Institute for Natural Family Planning: http://nfp.marquette.edu/
- ❖ Northwest Family Services: http://www.nwfs.org/couples-a-singles.html
- ❖ Creighton Model/FertilityCare: http://creightonmodel.com
- ❖ Standard Days and Two Day Method: http://www.irh.org

Method	Formula and Cycle Data	Cervical Fluid	Cervical Position	Basal Temperature	Hormonal Monitor	
Archdiocese of Boston Sympto-Hormonal Cross-Check	✓	✓		✓	✓	
Creighton Fertility Care		✓				
Couple to Couple Sympto-Thermal	✓	✓	✓	✓		
Billings		✓				

Visit www.BostonCatholic.org/NFP for:

❖ Why use NFP?

❖ How do I learn NFP?

❖ List of NFP sites

❖ Schedule of programs

❖ Links to more information

	Private Classes	Group Classes	Private Follow-up	English	Spanish	Portuguese	No. of classes in 6 months
	✓	✓	✓	✓	✓		4
	✓		✓	✓	✓		7
		✓	✓	✓			3
	✓		✓	✓	✓	✓	4

ACTIVITY

1. What had you heard before this presentation about NFP?

2. Did the presentation deepen your thinking about NFP? How?

3. What would be the benefits of learning NFP?

4. How will you be responsible and generous with your fertility?

5. Have you discussed as a couple that you might not be able to achieve pregnancy?

6. What are my expectations/hopes/anxieties for our sexual relationship?

7. What might we do in the months remaining before our marriage to prepare ourselves to live the Church's vision of marital sexuality?

8. If sexually active, please also answer the following questions:

   Have you considered abstinence until your wedding day?

   How would your wedding day be different if you were chaste before the wedding?

9. What issues do we still need to discuss? What questions do we still need to ask?

10. If living together, discuss together possible reasons.

    ❑ Test the relationship

    ❑ Thought it would strengthen the relationship

    ❑ Not ready to commit to marriage

    ❑ Save money

    ❑ Convenience

    ❑ Have a place to live

    ❑ Other: _____

11. Was there a previous reluctance/hesitation to marry? YES NO

12. If so, why? Is that now resolved?

13. Why are you now getting married?

    ❑ Ready to make a permanent commitment

    ❑ No longer hesitant

    ❑ Understand the difference marriage makes

    ❑ Pressure from family/friends

    ❑ Pressure from fiancé/e

    ❑ Pregnant

    ❑ Too late to start over

    ❑ Other: _____

14. Have you considered living apart until your wedding day?

15. How would your wedding day be different if you lived apart before the wedding?

MARITAL SEXUALITY RESOURCES

Generous and Responsible Parenthood

*Practical Advice for Discerning Your Family Size
and Dealing with Disagreement Around Family Planning*

"It seems inconsistent with the nature of God that he would want us to be fearful or anxious over the decision to have children. It seems more likely that God would like us to see the decision to have children the same way we might see a decision about whom we will marry—exciting, full of expectation, hopeful and passionate. The only way our discernment of parenthood will be these things to us is if we love our spouse generously and allow God into the discernment process in every possible way."[1]

1. Foster a loving attitude toward all children.
   ❖ "Once I worried about what I would have to give up in having children; now I know there is nothing that I would not give up for my children."[2]

2. Do not be afraid to stand up for your beliefs or desires and do so with patience, respect, and love.
   ❖ Have courage . . . you each have the right and obligation to continue to discuss these issues, resisting all temptation to turn topics that need to be unifying topics into divisive topics.

3. Pray. Discuss. Pray. Discuss . . . Agree.
   ❖ Pray and examine your own heart first. Then discuss and listen respectfully to each other. This cycle of praying and discussing needs to continue until you reach consensus.

4. Get your ducks and priorities in a row.
   ❖ Part of family planning is planning for a family. Make an honest, selfless consideration of your life as a couple and family.
   ❖ Are your relationship and family strong enough to support another member? In other words, is your marriage loving and intimate? If applicable, are the relationships among your existing children caring and supportive? Do you believe that you are capable of fulfilling the physical, spiritual, relational, and psychological responsibilities of your existing children and those of a new child?

---

1. Jason Adams, *Called to Give Life: A Sourcebook on the Blessing of Children and the Harm of Contraception* (Dayton, OH: One More Soul, 2003), 127.

2. Ibid., 126.

❖ If you can answer in the affirmative to these questions, it may be time to add to your "community of love." If you cannot answer in the affirmative to these questions, you may have an obligation to either address these issues before conceiving a child or while pursuing conception.

5. Keep the question of pregnancy open.

❖ Ask, "Are we to strengthen 'the community of love' that already exists or are we to add a new member to our already strong, loving family?"

❖ NFP helps keep the question open and helps couples to listen to their bodies in the discernment of parenthood. The desire for the marital act should not be thought of as only a physical impulse but also as a divine prompting toward openness to parenthood.

6. Seek appropriate assistance/support.

❖ Seek technical assistance in learning Natural Family Planning.

❖ Seek the intellectual support that comes from understanding what the Church really teaches and why.

❖ Seek spiritual support through prayer and frequent **reception** of the sacraments of Eucharist and Reconciliation.

❖ Seek emotional support through **counsel with others who un**derstand the Church's vision of marriage **and family.**

❖ If necessary, seek **professional support from a marriage counselor who shares** Catholic beliefs.

7. Strive to live a holy **life.**

❖ Striving to be **the person, couple, and family God wants you to be establishes an** environment in which you can be reasonably assured that you can be responsible and generous **with your combined fertility.**

The Love of Adoption

Dear Engaged Couples,

Congratulations on your engagement! We hope that this time of marriage preparation brings you much joy and quality time together.

We have fond memories of our own marriage preparation weekend as a time when we spent quality time together in the midst of the chaos of wedding planning. It was a time for us to dream and plan for our future. Like many young couples, we pictured a period of time in which we would enjoy our "couplehood" and then, after a year or two, begin our journey into parenthood. That was our plan . . . and then there was God's plan.

After about a year and a half of marriage (during which time we used Natural Family Planning in order to avoid pregnancy), we made the decision that we would try to conceive a child. For the next four years (during which we used NFP to help us achieve pregnancy), we rode an emotional roller coaster of hope and disappointment. We struggled watching our friends and family members announce the imminent births of their offspring.

Throughout this time, many physicians encouraged us to explore the many treatment options available through reproductive technology. Suddenly, we faced the challenges of evaluating the morality of each fertility treatment option that was presented to us. While we learned that there are some fertility treatments that our Catholic faith and beliefs did not oppose, our struggle ultimately led to the decision not to try any fertility treatment. We finally made the decision to explore adoption but continued to hold onto the hope that we would conceive naturally.

In September 1999, we submitted an application for domestic adoption. We struggled with mixed reactions from friends and family, which ranged from enthusiastic support to incredulous disapproval. What if the birth parents want to take the child back? What if the child has "issues"? How could we want to raise someone else's child? We were quickly made comfortable regarding the first two issues by educating ourselves about adoption, with help from the adoption professionals with whom we worked. Regarding "raising someone else's child," we knew from the extent to which we came to love and adore our friends' children, that we could most certainly love a child from a different gene pool than our own. (Look at how much many people come to cherish their pets, and they are not biologically related!)

In August 2000, we were notified that a birth mother had selected us to parent the baby she was expecting. For the next two weeks, as we awaited the birth of our first adopted child, we fell in love with the idea of a child whom we quickly came to think of and know as "our daughter." Born with significant health issues, the intensive care staff as well as the adoption agency staff went out of their way to warn us about all that could go wrong with her health if she were to live through the next month. But we were hooked. We had seen her, held her and prayed for her, and we knew with absolute certainty that she was the child who had grown so fully in our hearts throughout the previous six years. She is now healthy, sweet, and free of all of the worst case scenarios that the doctors tried to warn us about. Like many couples waiting to adopt, we held onto the hope of conception until the point that this child was placed in our arms. While we would be delighted to conceive a child, we are most definitely completely fulfilled as adoptive parents.

In the six years that followed our August 2000 launch into parenthood, we were profoundly blessed with three more amazing, beautiful, and bright adopted children (girl, boy, girl), including a biological sibling of our oldest daughter. All have been with us since their births. All of our children are aware that they are adopted and grew in "another mother's tummy," but they know with absolute certainty that they all grew in our hearts.

We often laugh when we hear the Garth Brooks song "Unanswered Prayers." In the first few years of our marriage, we stormed heaven with pleas to conceive a child of our own . . . but he knew best . . . and chose to answer our prayers another way. We know with absolute certainty that each of these four children was meant to be part of our family. We would not have wanted it any other way. (All this and no labor pains!)

Whether you are faced with the challenge of infertility or not, we hope and pray that you will give serious consideration to exploring the beautiful gift of adoption. It has blessed our lives profoundly!

Best wishes for a joyful future,

Mary Pat and Tom St. Jean

The Destructive Effects of Pornography on Marriage

By Bruce Hannemann, M.A., and Jeannie Hannemann, M.A.[3]

"My people are ruined for lack of knowledge." (Hosea 4:6)

"I wish that ten years ago someone had educated me on pornography: what it is, what it does, and what it reaches in and destroys in the hearts, minds, and bodies of men and women." Many such comments are the reason we feel compelled to include the following information on pornography in this marriage preparation program.

Cultural Influences and Staggering Statistics Seem to Normalize Pornography

Our culture makes it a challenge to avoid the hyper-sexuality that is found in the media and bombards us daily. Pornography has a seductive power that twists the God-given pleasure of intimacy into an unholy obsession. We frequently see sexual sin marketed and provocatively packaged in magazines, on the Internet, on television, and in movies. Lust is promoted in the media, joked about publicly and accepted as the norm. Here are some sobering statistics about pornography use:[4]

❖ Americans rent upward of 800 million pornographic videos and DVDs (about one in five of all rented movies is porn).

❖ The 11,000 porn films shot each year far outpaces Hollywood's yearly slate of 400.

❖ Four billion dollars a year is spent on video pornography in the United States, more than on football, baseball, and basketball.

❖ One in four Internet users looks at a pornography website in any given month.

❖ Men look at pornography online more than they look at any other subject.

❖ 66 percent of 18- to 34-year-old men visit a pornographic site every month.

❖ 47 percent of Christians say pornography is a major problem in the home.[5]

---

3. About the authors: At the request of Bishop David Ricken of the Diocese of Green Bay, Bruce and Jeannie Hannemann co-developed RECLAiM Sexual Health with experts in mental health, addiction recovery, neuroscience, online technology, *Theology of the Body*, and Church teaching. Combining *The Brain Science of Change*, insights from *Theology of the Body* and Church teaching, RECLAiM is an anonymous, online recovery program from pornography, masturbation, and other unhealthy sexual behaviors. For more information about the Hannemanns and their own recovery story, or the RECLAiM Sexual Health recovery program, please visit: *www.reclaimsexualhealth.com*.

4. Pamela Paul, "From Pornography to Porno to Porn: How Porn Became the Norm," in *The Social Costs of Pornography: A Collection of Papers*, James R. Stoner, Jr. and Donna M. Hughes, eds. (2010).

5. Archdiocese of Omaha Anti-Pornography Task Force pornography statistics, http://www.archomaha.org/postoral/se/pdf/PornStats.pdf (September 25, 2012).

Estimates indicate the number of people in the United States struggling with pornography and masturbation could be as high as 60 million or more. Our culture misleads us to believe that lust, pornography use, and masturbation are good activities that we need not be concerned about.

We Know Otherwise

Marriage statistics tell us otherwise. At an annual meeting of the American Academy of Matrimonial Lawyers, 62 percent said the Internet had been a significant factor in divorces they had handled during the last year. Lawyers polled indicated that 68 percent of the divorce cases involved one party meeting a new love interest over the Internet and 56 percent of the divorce cases involved one party having an obsessive interest in pornographic websites.[6]

Jesus tells us otherwise. Matthew 5:28 says: "But I say to you, everyone who looks at a woman with lust has already committed adultery with her in his heart."

Our Catholic Church tells us otherwise. "Pornography consists in removing real or simulated sexual acts from the intimacy of the partners, in order to display them deliberately to third parties. It offends against chastity because it perverts the conjugal act, the intimate giving of spouses to each other. It does grave injury to the dignity of its participants, (actors, vendors, the public), since each one becomes an object of base pleasure and illicit profit for others. It immerses all who are involved in the illusion of a fantasy world. It is a grave offense."[7]

We Also Know That Pornography Is Addicting

If you're straining under the negative effects of a porn obsession, you've likely tried to stop countless times, only to fall right back into the habit. That is because of this truth about pornography: viewing porn triggers such an intense neurochemical release in the brain that it can quickly create a literal "chemical dependency." As a result, many neuroscientists refer to pornography as the most powerful drug in history. The good news is that recovery programs now exist to help people break free from this type of addiction.

Pornography is addicting because:

❖ Pornography arouses sexual desire, which is usually followed by masturbation.

❖ Pornography and masturbation cause the body to release endogenous chemicals (such as dopamine, serotonin, and norepinephrine).

---

6. Jill Manning, Testimony, "Hearing on Pornography's Impact on Marriage & the Family," U.S. Senate Hearing: Subcommittee on the Constitution, Civil Rights and Property Rights, Committee on Judiciary, November 10, 2005 as accessed at http://s3.amazonaws.com/thf_media/2010/pdf/ManningTST.pdf on October 12, 2012.

7. CCC, no. 2354.

❖ These internal chemicals produce a powerful rush or high very similar to street drugs, and the human brain's pleasure center becomes addicted to this high.

❖ This sexual release is only temporary and an escalation of the behavior is needed in order to maintain sexual arousal. This leads to an escalation in unhealthy sexual behaviors.

❖ The neurochemical rush of pornography and masturbation can quickly become a convenient and instant "drug-of-choice" for pleasure, escape, and self-medication from loneliness, boredom, and the stresses of life. Over time, it can evolve into an internal "chemical dependency."

How Pornography and Masturbation Harm a Person and Marriage

Many people get married hoping it will cure their compulsion for pornography, fantasy, and masturbation. It does not. Thus, if you are getting married and have been engaging in these unhealthy sexual behaviors, you need to be aware of possible harmful consequences:

❖ Pornography and masturbation can affect intimacy. Pornography and masturbation lead a person to isolation and satisfying selfish needs. Masturbation is contrary to God's plan for sexuality to be self-giving with love. It is instead an act of self-pleasure with lust. It lacks the full meaning of human sexuality which is directed toward a loving, marital relationship.

❖ Pornography and masturbation can interfere with healthy sexuality in a marriage. Over time, "self-sex" can become your brain's "preferred" method for achieving sexual gratification. Repeated exposure to pornography leads a person to see others, including one's spouse, as objects. Healthy attachments and bonding can become difficult and can make connecting with others more difficult.

❖ Pornography also leads to fantasies that can control the user to the point where it can be extremely difficult to transition to healthy sexual behaviors. Escalating fantasies, images, and desires can take over everyday thoughts and behaviors. It can destroy the capacity to remain faithful in marriage.

❖ According to Dr. Mary Anne Layden, "Pornography viewers tend to have problems with premature ejaculation and erectile dysfunction. Having spent so much time in unnatural sexual experiences with paper, celluloid, and cyberspace, they seem to find it difficult to have sex with a real human being. Pornography is raising their expectation and demand for types and amounts of sexual experiences; at the same time it is reducing their ability to experience sex."[8] Erectile

---

8. Dr. Mary Anne Layden, U.S. Senate Testimony, "Hearing on the Brain Science Behind Pornography Addiction and the Effects of Addiction on Families and Communities," November 2004 as accessed at http://www.ccv.org/wp-content/uploads/2010/04/Judith_Reisman_Senate_Testimony-2004.11.18.pdf on October 12, 2012.

dysfunction can be a problem for newlyweds when the husband has a history of masturbation. As a result, some couples are not even able to consummate their marriage.

❖ Pornography and masturbation can affect other areas of life. A person addicted to pornography loses the ability to experience pleasure in the ordinary life circumstances of marriage. In addition, pornography and masturbation can lead a person to look at all aspects of life from a selfish, lustful point of view. This harms marriage, family, financial stability, and careers.

❖ Keep in mind that pornography, fantasy, and masturbation are forms of "adultery of the heart" whether you are doing it alone or as a couple. Even couples who view pornography together harm their intimacy.

From this list, we hope it is evident that all forms of pornography, fantasy, and masturbation–past, present, or future–have the potential to harm your marriage. These unhealthy sexual behaviors put you in serious emotional, physical, relational, and spiritual danger. Sexual sin of any type and extent creates wounds that affect the body, mind, and spirit. So, it is imperative that you address this issue immediately.

What Can You Do?

❖ *Talk to each other:* This may be difficult and embarrassing, but keep in mind that honesty and trust is the foundation of any good marriage. If you need help to overcome this problem, it is much better to get it before marriage than to wait until marital problems overwhelm you. Prepare for your wedding day by following what Scripture says: "Immorality or any impurity or greed must not even be mentioned among you, as is fitting among holy ones" (Ephesians 5:3).

❖ *Seek the help you need:* Since many people begin this type of obsession because of a sexual trauma, such as abuse or exposure to pornography at a young age, you will need to address those wounds. This may require some professional therapy. Others stumble across pornographic images on the Internet or read a romance novel and are hooked on the world of fantasy and masturbation. Either way, you can find hope and a way out! Your brain is "neuroplastic," which means it can be shaped, molded, and changed. You are not stuck with your old addiction circuitry. You can learn to work with your brain's natural built-in mechanisms for positive change through recovery programs.

❖ *Go to the sacrament of Reconciliation:* God is eager to forgive all sins and provide grace to help heal from the wounds and overcome the sin in the future.

❖ *Consider waiting to wed:* Talk to those helping you prepare for marriage and professionals in the field as you discern your readiness and ability to commit yourselves to each other in marriage. An addiction to pornography may be a reason to pause in your preparations. Talk to others and each other about this option.

Do Not Fear!

Trust in God and look forward to the joy and happiness that awaits you as an individual and couple once freed from the harmful effects of pornography and masturbation. Freedom, peace, joy, and much love await you!

We Are on a Mission

To Guard, Reveal,
and Communicate Love:
Making Sure Our Marriage
Lasts a Lifetime

"The family has the mission
to guard, reveal, and
communicate love."

Familiaris Consortio, no. 17

HOUSE METAPHOR

ﻼ Just as a house requires regular maintenance to avoid problems and may sometimes need expert assistance, so too, a marriage requires regular attention and may sometimes need expert assistance.

GOALS

ﻼ *Be wise* and *be skilled*: To suggest areas where you can guard your love by establishing healthy boundaries.

ﻼ *Be true*, *be skilled*, and *be faithful*: To help you consider ways to reveal and communicate love throughout your lifetime.

ﻼ *Be true* and *be faithful*: To encourage you to persevere despite any difficulties that may come.

Guard love by establishing healthy boundaries

❖ We can guard love within marriage by establishing and maintaining healthy boundaries.

❖ Just as a fence provides protection and establishes boundaries, so too we must establish and maintain boundaries to guard our love and unity.

Work

❖ While work is necessary, we can't protect our love and unity if we are never home or when we are emotionally disconnected.

❖ Work provides meaning and financial support, but it cannot come before our nuclear family and God.

❖ Our occupation has to serve both our nuclear family and our relationship with God.

Extended family

❖ Marriage reconfigures existing relationships while establishing a brand new one.

❖ As married couples, we must not abandon our parents and siblings, but recognize we have a new family.

- Marriage calls for a change in our relationship with our parents.
- Their role in our lives will need to be both honored and modified.

Friends

- Friendships that nurture your family life should be sought after.
- Not every friend may share your values regarding marriage and family.
- Some friendships can take you away from time spent emotionally connecting with family.

Entertainment/Leisure

- While leisure is essential to a balanced life, in excess it can drain precious hours away from marriage and family.
- Certain entertainments, i.e. novels, magazines, and movies, can cause us to have unrealistic expectations for marriage.

Relationships with the opposite sex

- Be aware of interactions with people of the opposite sex, especially in work environments.
- Don't be surprised by an attraction to someone other than your spouse.
- This is natural and does not mean you have married the wrong person.
- Such attraction does not mean you have to dwell or act on the attraction.
- Do not give the attraction a second thought. Do what is needed to avoid the temptation. Be prepared. Draw on the graces of the sacraments of Marriage and Reconciliation.

Social media

- Social media can be a good thing.
- We need to pay attention, however, to both how much time we spend and how we actually interact with others through these avenues.
- Social media outlets are an increasingly important area to address and in which to set healthy boundaries.
- Consider some technology-free times as a couple.

As parents

❖ Parents can guard love within the family by being the primary educators of their children.

❖ A child's first education in love and marriage begins in the family.

❖ Parents are responsible to see that their children are nurtured and that they receive solid human and spiritual formation.

❖ Parents can also guard love within the family by both setting healthy boundaries for their children and helping their children to set boundaries.

Examples:

— Helping children balance all their responsibilities and activities so that there is time for family interaction.

— Ensuring children have friends who support the family values.

— Guiding them in establishing healthy relationships with the opposite sex.

— Helping children use social media appropriately.

Reveal love

"The family, like the Church, ought to be a place where the Gospel is transmitted and from which the Gospel radiates."[1]

❖ Our lives, marriage, and family are supposed to radiate God's love.

❖ That is what the Gospel is—the story of God's love for us as revealed by the life, death, and resurrection of Jesus.

❖ Our lives are supposed to reveal this love, *agape* love.

Communicate love

❖ Remember that *agape* is the type of love that will last a lifetime.

❖ *Agape* is unconditional and sacrificial love. It is a choice. It leads us to consider the good of the other.

❖ Think how healthy, happy, and holy your marriage and family would be if you choose to be loving on a daily, weekly, and annual basis—even when you don't feel like it!

---

1. John Paul II, *Familiaris Consortio* (Boston: Pauline Books & Media, 1981), no. 52.

Daily

- *As spouses:* Do something that your spouse appreciates, not necessarily something you appreciate—just for her or him.
- *Ideas:* Make coffee, do the laundry, clean the toilet, put a note in his or her lunch, say "I love you," intentionally listen even when you don't feel like it, share daily events.
- *As parents:* Do something that demonstrates to your children that they are valued and loved.
- *Ideas:* Put a note in a lunch, say "I love you," talk to them, ask how their day was, make dinner, etc.

Weekly

- *As spouses:* Couple time every week deepens intimacy and generates excitement and anticipation.
- It may be easy to do at first, but it takes regular planning to keep it a lifelong habit, especially after you have children.
- *Ideas:* Date night, couch time, early breakfast, or late dinner together.
- *As parents:* Time spent together as a family or "special time" with each child is priceless.
- *Ideas:* game nights, outside activities, Sunday Mass, car time, bedtime.

Annually

- *As spouses:* Make a decision to invest in your marriage annually in a significant way.
- *Ideas:* Celebrate anniversaries, take a couple vacation or get away—even for twenty-four hours, attend a marriage seminar, workshop, or retreat.
- *As parents:* Do your best to create memorable annual events and traditions.
- *Ideas:* family vacations, plant a tree for significant events, create memories, i.e., purchase Christmas tree ornaments while on vacation, create photo albums.

Persevere in love

- ❖ Difficulties and trials are inevitable.
- ❖ Despite our efforts to communicate, guard, and reveal love, all marriages and families will have difficulties and trials.
- ❖ Suffering is a part of the human condition.
- ❖ While we are obliged to do what we can to morally alleviate suffering reasonably, such as using medicine or offering assistance, there are some difficulties we cannot easily remedy.
- ❖ If we cannot alleviate suffering it may be possible to find meaning in it and use it as a means to grow in virtue and love.

Jesus is both a model for us *and* the means for us to handle our difficulties and trials.

- ❖ Model: Jesus accepted suffering, indeed entering into all the suffering any person has undergone or will undergo, he didn't run from it.
  - — He suffered for us united with the Father, and great merits were obtained from it—our salvation.
- ❖ Means: The cross teaches us that we are not alone in our difficulties.
  - — Jesus already shares our human suffering.
  - — Through the sacraments we receive his grace and strength.
  - — His Spirit helps us to persevere in the midst of our trials.

We can "offer up" our trials as prayers.

- ❖ "Offering things up" means to take any suffering, annoyance, difficulty, or sacrifice and offer them as prayers to God.
- ❖ Just as merits were obtained through the sufferings of Christ, we are asking that our suffering be used to obtain merits for a purpose or person.
- ❖ For example, if someone breaks an ankle, he or she can offer the pain and inconvenience for growth in patience, for their aunt's health, their marriage, etc.
- ❖ Saints are great role models in teaching us how not to "waste suffering." Their lives were often filled with sufferings that they offered to Christ and from which great merits were gained.

"Let us . . . persevere in running the race that lies before us" (Hebrews 12:1).

- ❖ We vow the day of our wedding, "in good times and in bad."
- ❖ Share each other's burdens.

If needed, seek help to love well

- ❖ Sometimes we need help to love well.

- ❖ Just as houses sometimes require outside expertise, i.e., leaky roof, flooded basement, our marriage or family may sometimes need outside assistance.

- ❖ It is good to talk to people we trust for sincere advice and guidance, but be careful of just venting to others, friends, family, etc.

- ❖ If help is needed, speak to people who can help.

- ❖ Some areas that usually require outside assistance:

    — Domestic violence

    — Addictions of all types (substance abuse, pornography, gambling)

    — Infidelity

    — Financial difficulties

    — Mental illness

    — Unresolved parental/child conflict

    — Unresolved issues that keep surfacing

Helpful resources

- ❖ U.S. Bishops website: www.ForYourMarriage.org.

- ❖ Retrouvaille: www.HelpOurMarriage.org.

- ❖ Marriage seminar

- ❖ Marriage and family counseling

- ❖ Priest

- ❖ Family and friends

TAKE HOME ACTIVITY
COMMUNICATING LOVE

Think about your future spouse . . .

1. What do you think *he or she would like* you to do on a *daily* basis as an expression of your love for him or her?

_____

_____

_____

_____

_____

2. What do you think *he or she would like* you to do together on a *weekly* basis as an expression of your love for one another?

_____

_____

_____

_____

_____

3. What do you think *he or she would like* you to do together on an *annual* basis as an expression of your love for one another?

_____

_____

_____

_____

_____

What about you . . .

4. What *would you like your spouse* to do on a *daily* basis as an expression of his/her love for you?

_____

_____

_____

_____

_____

5. What *would you like* to do together on a *weekly* basis as an expression of your love for one another?

_____

_____

_____

_____

_____

6. What *would you like* to do together on an *annual* basis as an expression of your love for one another?

_____

_____

_____

_____

_____

TAKE HOME ACTIVITY
GUARDING AND PERSEVERING
IN LOVE AS A MARRIED COUPLE

Directions: Pick a quiet time and place to discuss these questions together.
Recommendation: Review these questions once a year, perhaps on or near your anniversary!

Work

- Am I working so much that my marriage and family suffer?
- Am I not working enough to provide?
- How does my work affect intimacy with my spouse and children? With God?
- What do I miss because of work?

Extended Family

- Am I putting my parent's opinions above my spouse's?
- Am I putting the needs of my family of origin above the needs of my nuclear family?
- Am I investing more in one extended family than the other?
- Am I neglecting either extended family?

Friends

- Am I selective about soliciting advice and support from friends?
- Am I spending too much time and emotional energy on friendships?
- Do we have both individual and mutual friends who support our vocation to marriage?
- Are my interactions with friends serving and supporting my relationship with God, my marriage, and my family?

Entertainment/leisure

- Do I make time to rest?
- Am I spending too much time in leisure pursuits?
- Are my choices for recreation good choices?
- Do I consider the interests of my spouse when choosing leisure pursuits?

- Do I currently have unhealthy relationships with people of the opposite sex?
- Am I prone to neglect healthy boundaries with persons of the opposite sex?

Social media

- Are my social media interactions respectful of my marriage?
- Do my social media interactions take away needed time and energy?

Difficulties and Trials

- Are we committed to persevere in times of difficulties and trials?
- Do we practice "offering up" our trials?
- Do I communicate difficulties to my spouse or vent to others?

Seeking help, if needed, to love well

- Are there things in our marriage that we are unable to resolve?
- Do we need outside assistance?
- Am I willing to seek outside assistance?

PERSONAL NOTES

Program Wrap-Up

Transformed in Love:
Putting on the Finishing Touches

"Unless the LORD build the house,
they labor in vain who build."

PSALM 127:1

A Catholic marriage transformed in love . . .

1. Is made of mature, virtuous, self-giving individuals.

2. Is one in which spouses communicate well and develop deep intimacy.

3. Is one in which expectations are well managed.

4. Is one in which husband and wife choose to love one another with *agape* love, seeking the good of the other.

5. Is one in which the spouses respect the nature and purposes of marriage.

6. Is one that is transformed by and radiates the love of Jesus.

7. Is one in which husband and wife are committed to their vows and live them out.

8. Is one that has a unified Christian approach to finances that is both generous and responsible.

9. Is one in which husband and wife keep first things first and engage regularly in spiritual practices as individuals, a couple, and a family.

10. Is one open to God's grace and presence and is centered in the Eucharist.

11. Is one in which sexual intimacy is cherished and couples are both generous and responsible with fertility.

12. Is one in which spouses persevere in guarding, revealing, and communicating love.

13. Is one in which husband and wife are transformed by God's love.

Ten Things to Do Between Now and Our Wedding Day to Be More Transformed in Love

- ❏ Attend weekly Mass.
- ❏ Go to confession before our wedding.
- ❏ Pray together.
- ❏ Embrace chastity.
- ❏ Enroll in an NFP class.
- ❏ Practice communication skills.
- ❏ Create a unified financial plan.
- ❏ Volunteer together.
- ❏ Review the list of red flags in the "Letter from the Tribunal" in Topic 7 (pp. 61–63), and if any are identified, seek assistance.
- ❏ Be intentional about final preparations, including liturgical preparations and meetings with the priest/deacon preparing us for marriage.

OUR MARITAL BLUEPRINT

1.

2.

3.

4.

5.

6.

7.

8.

9.

10.

11.

12.

13.

OUR PERSONAL MARITAL BLUEPRINT

Topic 1: Self-Knowledge
Who Am I? Who Are You? We Are the Builders

The most helpful thing for me about this topic was:

The one thing I want to do as a result of this topic is:

Topic 2: Communication
Our Relationship Needs Some TLC: Skills for Building

The most helpful thing for me about this topic was:

The one thing I want to do as a result of this topic is:

Topic 3: Expectations
What Are We Expecting? What Will Our Marriage Be Like?

The most helpful thing for me about this topic was:

The one thing I want to do as a result of this topic is:

Topic 4: What Is Love?
Seeking the Good of the Other: Making Our House a Home

The most helpful thing for me about this topic was:

The one thing I want to do as a result of this topic is:

Topic 5: What Is Marriage?
God's Plan for Love and Life: The Architect's Design

The most helpful thing for me about this topic was:

The one thing I want to do as a result of this topic is:

Topic 6: What Is Sacramental Marriage?
You, Me, and Jesus: Our Marriage Transformed by and Radiating His Love

The most helpful thing for me about this topic was:

The one thing I want to do as a result of this topic is:

Topic 7: The Rite of Marriage
I Do, Do You?: The Promises We Make and Live

The most helpful thing for me about this topic was:

The one thing I want to do as a result of this topic is:

Topic 8: Finances
Yours, Mine, OURS: Resources for Marriage and Family Life

The most helpful thing for me about this topic was:

The one thing I want to do as a result of this topic is:

Topic 9: Eight Spiritual Practices for Marriage and Family Life
Nurturing Faith: Building a Firm Foundation

The most helpful thing for me about this topic was:

The one thing I want to do as a result of this topic is:

Topic 10: The Teaching Mass
The Presence of Christ: The Cornerstone of Our Marriage

The most helpful thing for me about this topic was:

Thc one thing I want to do as a result of this topic is:

Topic 11: Marital Sexuality
A Divine Design: The Architect's Plan to Nurture Love and Life

The most helpful thing for me about this topic was:

The one thing I want to do as a result of this topic is:

Topic 12: We Are on a Mission
To Guard, Reveal, and Communicate Love: Making Sure Our Marriage Lasts a Lifetime

The most helpful thing for me about this topic was:

The one thing I want to do as a result of this topic is:

Overall Program

Transformed in Love: Building Your Catholic Marriage

The most helpful thing for me about this marriage preparation program was:

The one thing I want to do as a result of this marriage preparation program is:

Things we would like to talk about with the priest/deacon/ pastoral associate preparing us for marriage:

Go back through your activities or your list of reflections and list any topics/questions/ concerns you would like to bring to the priest, deacon, or pastoral associate preparing you for marriage:

_____

_____

_____

_____

_____

_____

_____

_____

_____

_____

_____

_____

_____

_____

SMALL GROUP DISCUSSION GUIDE

1. Gather with tablemates or those nearby.

2. If you would like to, share one or both of your answers to either question regarding the topics covered in this meeting *(it is not obligatory to speak)*.

    The most helpful thing for me about this topic was . . .

    The one thing I want to do as a result of this topic is . . .

3. Share the reasons for your answers.

4. After everyone has shared, pick one or two things to share with the large group or individuals may share thoughts not shared in the small group.

Pauline
BOOKS & MEDIA

A mission of the Daughters of St. Paul

As apostles of Jesus Christ, evangelizing today's world:

We are CALLED to holiness
by God's living Word and Eucharist.

We COMMUNICATE the Gospel message
through our lives and through all
available forms of media.

We SERVE the Church
by responding to the hopes and needs
of all people with the Word of God,
in the spirit of St. Paul.

For more information visit us at www.pauline.org.

Pauline
BOOKS & MEDIA

The Daughters of St. Paul operate book and media centers at the following addresses. Visit, call, or write the one nearest you today, or find us at www.pauline.org

¡También somos su fuente para libros,
videos y música en español!